1972
9—

1972
9—

וּלְשׁוֹנֵנוּ רִנָּה

THE SONGS WE SING

וּלְשׁוֹנֵנוּ רִנָּה

THE

Selected and Edited by

Illustrations by

K. OECHSLI

NEW YORK 1950 ÷ 5710

SONGS WE SING

HARRY COOPERSMITH

The United Synagogue Commission on Jewish Education

Designed by P. OLDENBURG

English Summaries by D. PESSIN

DEDICATED TO

*my wife, Ethel and
my daughter, Penina*

Preface

JEWISH SONG — hardly ever absent from the hearts and mouths of our people — has, of late, experienced a real renaissance. The rise of the Nationalist Movement, culminating, at long last, in the establishment of the State of Israel; the upsurge of religious feeling, especially during the war years; an awakened concern on the part of educators and parents for the development of an integrated Jewish personality through a curriculum providing for emotional as well as intellectual growth — these are the forces most responsible for this renewed outpouring of a rich and variegated folk and art song.

Though many fine collections, reflecting that resurgence, have been published within recent years, they do not, for varying reasons, quite meet the overall needs of the school and the community. This book is an attempt to meet those needs by including sufficient and varied song material — old and new — for a six-year school curriculum, for the average home and community, and even, to some extent, for the performing artist and cantor.

A number of new songs have been created especially for this book and are here published for the first time. Others, though published elsewhere, have been included because of their great popularity. Some of the latter group will be remembered by parents from their own childhood. It is so that parents and children may sing together and experience the warm feeling of continuity that such songs are here included.

Every song in this book has been provided with a full, rich piano accompaniment. Many of these, as well as of the completely original compositions, represent the work of the most outstanding Jewish musicians here and abroad. The only restriction imposed on these musicians in their work was that they make the accompaniments simple.

Phrasing, dynamic marks, pedaling and fingering have been eliminated partly for aesthetic reasons but especially to allow freedom of interpretation.

A goodly number of these songs have singable translations. For the others, free, poetic English summaries are provided.

The songs in all except four sub-sections are arranged in the order of their difficulty, beginning with the simplest. (In "Grace After Meals" and "Songs from the Sabbath Service" the songs follow the order of the Prayer Book; in "High Holy Days" they follow the order of the Maḥzor; In "Passover" the order of the Hagada; and in "Biblical and Historical Songs" — the chronological order.)

The Sephardic pronunciation was used in the transliteration of secular songs and the Ashkenazic pronunciation for songs taken from the liturgy. The system of transliteration used is a simple one, derived from years of experience with non-Hebrew readers. Consistency within the system was violated, however, when good sense dictated.

It is in the nature of a book such as this to involve the efforts of many people, to all of whom I am deeply grateful. I am especially indebted to the many composers, poets and arrangers — both here and in Israel — and to the many translators and publishers who have given generously of their work; and to my friends and colleagues — Dr. A. M. Dushkin, Dr. B. M. Edidin (*Alav Ha-Shalom*), Dr. E. Gamoran (the original stimulator of this project), and Mr. & Mrs. I. B. Rappoport, for their many fruitful suggestions; to Mr. G. Ephros, for directing me to much pertinent material for the High Holiday section; to Mr. L. Kopf, for going over the manuscript; to Mr. R. Kosakoff, for a careful reading of the accompaniments and many wise suggestions with regard to them; to Mr. E. Indelman, for proof-reading the Hebrew texts; to Miss L. M. Jaffa, my former assistant, and Mr. J. Grossman, my present assistant, for their help in preparing the manuscript; to the many music teachers who helped with the proof-reading; and to the Jacob Michael Library, for photo-offsetting many of the songs derived from inaccessible sources.

My thanks go, too, to the Committee on Music of the United Synagogue Commission on Jewish Education — Rabbi Ario Hyams, chairman; Mrs. Judith K. Eisenstein; Cantor David Putterman; Cantor Robert Segal; and Rabbi Edward Sandrow, for their critical reaction to the selection of the material; and lastly my profound appreciation goes to Dr. Abraham E. Millgram, the Educational Director of the United Synagogue of America, for his ardent and understanding support throughout the difficult stages of this undertaking and for his dynamic interest and help in seeing the project through.

It is our earnest hope that the love and enthusiasm for these songs felt by those who created *Ulshonenu Rinah — The Songs We Sing* — will be conveyed through these pages, bringing a wealth of pleasure to both singer and listener.

HARRY COOPERSMITH

New York, October, 1949

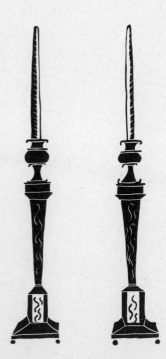

VIII

Acknowledgements

THE EDITOR and the publisher wish to make acknowledgements and express their appreciation to the following for composing songs especially for this book: Leonard Bernstein — *Yigdal*; Isidore Freed — *Haneros Halolu*; Herbert Fromm — *L'shana Tova, El Hasade*, Giver of All; Max Helfman — Colossus, Early Will I Seek Thee; Heinrich Schalit — Sabbath Eve, Song of Dedication; and to the following for creating piano accompaniments especially for this book: Hugo C. Adler — *Bo'olom Habo, M'nuho V'simho, Sim Sholom*; Herman Berlinski — *Av Horahamim*; Julius Chajes — *Shavu'a Tov*; Gershon Ephros — *L'ho Dodi*; Herbert Fromm — *Eli Tziyon*; Julius Grossman — *Yismah Moshe*; Frederick Jacobi — *Yishtaber V'yitromem*; Leah M. Jaffa — *Kadima Hapo'el*; Erwin Jospe — *Hanita*; Leo Kopf — *Hashivenu Eleha, Yigdal, Etz Hayim Hi*; Reuven Kosakoff — *Ato Ehod, Yo Ribon, Hamavdil, Bamidbar, Am Yisrael Hai*; Trude Rittman — *Plada K'hula, Ki Mitziyon*; Hyman Reznick — *Anu Olim*; Robert Starer — Hora from Sarid, *Ari Ara, Mi Yivne Hagalil, Debka*; Heinrich Schalit — *Al Tira Avdi Ya'akov, Ani Ma'amin*; Eric Werner — *Shir Lanegev, Kineret*; and to the following publishers and composers for permission to reprint songs from their publications: Behrman House, New York, for Open the Gates, Harvest, My Candles, Purim Greetings, Mordecai's Procession, Sailing Song, *S'vivon* — all from *The Gateway to Jewish Song* by Judith K. Eisenstein, and for permission to use many of the English summaries prepared by D. Pessin for *Songs of Zion* by Harry Coopersmith; Bloch Publishing Company, New York, for *V'shomru* from *Hibbat Shabbat, Had Gadyo* from *Seder Melodies, Nigun Bialik* from *New Palestine Folk Songs*, Vol. I, and *Ashre Ha'ish* from *New Palestine Folk Songs*, Vol. II — all by A. W. Binder; Central Conference of American Rabbis for *Shir Hama'alos, V'al Kulom* and True Freedom — all arranged by A. W. Binder and for his *Mi Homoho*; for *L'ho Adonoi* by Gershon Ephros, God Supreme by Joseph Achron and Sound the Loud Timbrel by Jacob Weinberg — all from the *Union Hymnal*; to Gershon Ephros for *Sh'ma Yisro'el, Zohrenu, Ovinu Malkenu, L'shono Tovo, Oleynu, Un'sane Tokef*

from *Cantorial Anthology*, Vol. I (published by Bloch); Simon and Schuster Inc., for Glee Reigns in Galilee from *The Fireside Book of Folksongs* (Copyright, 1947); to I. & J. Eisenstein for *V'taher Libenu* from the Cantata *Seven Golden Buttons*; to The Jewish Publication Society for *Birkas Hamozon* from *Sabbath the Day of Delight* by Abraham E. Millgram; Jewish Education Committee of New York for songs and translations too numerous to list, taken from *Choral Books of Jewish Songs, Sabbath and Festival Songsters, Primary and Kindergarten Songster, Sabbath Service in Song*, all compiled and edited by Harry Coopersmith; also for the Bible songs created for the old Bureau of Jewish Education by S. E. Goldfarb and S. S. Grossman and now the property of the Jewish Education Committee; for six new songs by Elchanan Indelman and Nahum Nardi (Copyright by National Artists Bureau, 1949) commissioned by the Jewish Education Committee of New York and published here for the first time; Hebrew Publishing Company for *L'shono Habo'o* from *Haggadah of Passover*, music by Moshe Nathanson; Israel Music Foundation through its representative Rev. Martin Adolph for the melodies of *Shir Lanegev* and *Kineret* which appeared in their record album; Jewish Songster Publishing Company for *Sholom Alehem, Mogen Ovos*, Zion our Mother, A Song of Zion, Longing for Jerusalem, At the Dawn, Hear the Voice from the *Jewish Songster*, Volumes I and II, by I. and S. E. Goldfarb; Edward B. Marks Music Corp. for *Kaha Kah* and *En Harod* (adapted to the poem Book of Books) from *Songs of the Pioneers*, arranged by A. W. Binder; Masada and Hehalutz Youth Zionist Organization through their representative M. S. Taylor for *Kuma Eha* arranged by E. W Sternberg, *Havu L'venim* arranged by Kurt Weil, and *Gam Hayom* arranged by Darius Milhaud; Metro Music Company for *Rozinkes Mit Mandlen* arranged by Zavel Zilberts and for the melody of *Yam Lied* by M. Schneyer; National Artist Bureau for *Aley Giva, Shir Avoda, Mi Yivne, Kemah* by Nahum Nardi (Copyright by composer, 1940); Heinrich Schalit for seven songs from his cantata, *Oley Tsiyon* and *Boney Tsiyon*; G. Schirmer Inc. for *Kadshenu* from

X

Contents

Songs from the Sabbath Evening Service

Songs from the Sabbath Morning Service

Havdala and M'lave Malka

XII

High Holy Days

Sukkot and Simḥat Torah

Ḥanukah

Passover

Lag Ba'omer

Shavuot

Tishah B'av

II. SONGS OF ISRAEL—וּבָאוּ צִיּוֹן בְּרִנָּה

Aliyah

Love of Land

Love of Land (Continued)

Ḥalutzim

Labor

Labor *(Continued)*

Israeli Dances

Directions for the dance steps to the above songs may be found in the following books: *Dances for Jewish Festivals* by D'vora Lapson pub. by the Jewish Educ. Comm. of N. Y.; *Palestine Dances* by Corinne Chacham pub. by Behrman House, N. Y.; *Jewish Folk Dance Book* by Delakova-Berk pub. by the Jewish Welfare Board, N. Y.

III. FAVORITE SONGS—OLD AND NEW—נְרַנְּנָה וְנִשְׂמְחָה בְּכָל יָמֵינוּ

Favorite Songs — Hebrew and Yiddish

Favorite Songs — English

Biblical and Historical Songs

Songs for Special Occasions

Bible Cantillations and Prayer Motifs

ולְשׁוֹנֵנוּ רְנָּה

THE SONGS WE SING

חַגִּים וּזְמַנִּים לְשָׁשׂוֹן

SABBATH AND HOLIDAY SONGS

SHABBAT KODESH

Moderato

Sha-bat ko-desh ma-ḥar ken, ken, ken, ken, ken. V'ḥalot sha-bat li od en, En, en, en, O - fe, o - fe ke-maḥ hey,
Hey, hey, hey, hey, hey. Ḥalot Sha-bat lanu a - se, A - se, a - se, a - se.

Tomorrow is the holy Sabbath. Bake me ḥalot, baker, please; catch me fish, O fisherman; bring me candles, peddler, pray; bartender, fill my jug with wine.

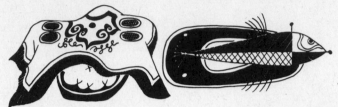

שַׁבַּת קֹדֶשׁ מָחָר כֵּן,
כֵּן, כֵּן, כֵּן, כֵּן.
וְחַלּוֹת שַׁבָּת לִי עוֹד אֵין,
אֵין, אֵין, אֵין.
אוֹפָה, אוֹפָה, קֶמַח הָא,
הָא, הָא, הָא, הָא, הָא.
חַלּוֹת שַׁבָּת לָנוּ עֲשֵׂה,
עֲשֵׂה, עֲשֵׂה, עֲשֵׂה.

Sha-bat ko-desh ma-ḥar ken,
    Ken, ken, ken, ken.
Da-gim l'Sha-bat li od en
    En, en, en.
Da-yag, da-yag, re-shet hey,
    Hey, hey, hey, hey, hey.
Da-gim l'Sha-bat li ho-tze,
    Ho-tze, ho-tze, ho-tze.

שַׁבַּת קֹדֶשׁ מָחָר כֵּן,
כֵּן, כֵּן, כֵּן, כֵּן.
נֵרוֹת שַׁבָּת לִי עוֹד אֵין,
אֵין, אֵין, אֵין.
רוֹכֵל, רוֹכֵל, כֶּסֶף הָא,
הָא, הָא, הָא, הָא, הָא.
נֵרוֹת שַׁבָּת לִי הָבֵא,
הָבֵא, הָבֵא, הָבֵא.

Sha-bat ko-desh ma-ḥar ken,
    Ken, ken, ken, ken.
Ne-rot Sha-bat li od en,
    En, en, en.
Ro-ḥel, ro-ḥel, ke-sef hey,
    Hey, hey, hey, hey, hey.
Ne-rot Sha-bat li ha-vey,
    Ha-vey, ha-vey, ha-vey.

שַׁבַּת קֹדֶשׁ מָחָר כֵּן,
כֵּן, כֵּן, כֵּן, כֵּן.
דָּגִים לְשַׁבָּת לִי עוֹד אֵין,
אֵין, אֵין, אֵין.
דַּיָּג, דַּיָּג, רֶשֶׁת הָא,
הָא, הָא, הָא, הָא, הָא.
דָּגִים לְשַׁבָּת לִי הוֹצֵא,
הוֹצֵא, הוֹצֵא, הוֹצֵא.

Sha-bat ko-desh ma-ḥar ken,
    Ken, ken, ken, ken.
Ya-yin l'ki-dush li od en,
    En, en, en.
Mo-zeg, mo-zeg, bak-buk hey,
    Hey, hey, hey, hey, hey.
Ya-yin l'ki-dush o-to ma-ley,
    Ma-ley, ma-ley, ma-ley.

שַׁבַּת קֹדֶשׁ מָחָר כֵּן,
כֵּן, כֵּן, כֵּן, כֵּן.
יַיִן לְקִדּוּשׁ לִי עוֹד אֵין,
אֵין, אֵין, אֵין.
מוֹזֵג, מוֹזֵג, בַּקְבּוּק הָא,
הָא, הָא, הָא, הָא, הָא.
יַיִן לְקִדּוּשׁ אוֹתוֹ מַלֵּא,
מַלֵּא, מַלֵּא, מַלֵּא.

BA'A SHABBAT

Peacefully

Ba-a Sha-bat, ba-a Sha-bat, Ba-a ba-a m'-nu-ha...........

Ba-a Sha-bat, ba-a Sha-bat, Ba-a, ba-a m'nu-ha........... M'nu-ha v'-sim-ha,

m'nu-ha v'-sim-ha B'yom ha-Sha-bat m'-nu-ha........... M'nu-ha v'-sim-ha,

m'nu-ha v'-sim-ha B'yom ha-Sha-bat m'-nu-ha........... B'yom ha-Sha-bat m'-nu-ha.

The Sabbath has come with peace and joy.

בָּאָה שַׁבָּת, בָּאָה שַׁבָּת,
בָּאָה, בָּאָה מְנוּחָה. (2)
מְנוּחָה וְשִׂמְחָה, מְנוּחָה וְשִׂמְחָו
בְּיוֹם הַשַּׁבָּת מְנוּחָה. (2)

SHABBAT HAMALKA

SABBATH QUEEN

We've welcomed the Sabbath with song and
  with prayer;
And home we return, our heart's gladness
  to share.
The table is set and the candles are lit,
The tiniest corner for Sabbath made fit.
O day of blessing, day of rest!
Sweet day of peace be ever blest!
Bring ye also peace, ye angels of peace!

הַחַמָּה מֵרֹאשׁ הָאִילָנוֹת נִסְתַּלְּקָה,
בֹּאוּ וְנֵצֵא לִקְרַאת שַׁבָּת הַמַּלְכָּה.
הִנֵּה הִיא יוֹרֶדֶת הַקְּדוֹשָׁה הַבְּרוּכָה,
וְעִמָּהּ מַלְאָכִים צְבָא שָׁלוֹם וּמְנוּחָה.
בֹּאִי, בֹּאִי, הַמַּלְכָּה,
בֹּאִי, בֹּאִי, הַכַּלָּה,
שָׁלוֹם עֲלֵיכֶם, מַלְאֲכֵי הַשָּׁלוֹם.

SABBATH EVE

Moderato, with devotion

Come, O ho-ly Sab-bath eve-ning, Crown my toil with well earned rest, Bring me hal-lowed hours of glad-ness, Days of days be-loved and blest..... Come, O ho-ly Sab-bath spir-it, Ra-diant shine from eve-ry eye,.... Give to all man-

kind a fore-taste Of our spi-rit's home on high.

HADLOKAS NER SHEL SHABBOS

Bo- ruḥ a - to A-do-noi.... e - lo - -he-nu me-leḥ ho-o-

tom.... a - sher kid-sho-nu b' - mitz-vo-sov, a - sher kid-sho-nu b'-

mitz - vo - sov v' - tzi - - vo - nu l' - - had - lik ner shel Sha - - bos.....

Blessed art Thou, O Lord, who hast commanded
us to kindle the Sabbath lights.

בָּרוּךְ אַתָּה יְיָ אֱלֹהֵינוּ מֶלֶךְ הָעוֹלָם
אֲשֶׁר קִדְּשָׁנוּ בְּמִצְוֹתָיו וְצִוָּנוּ
לְהַדְלִיק נֵר שֶׁל שַׁבָּת.

SHOLOM ALEḤEM

Peace unto you, O angels of peace. May your
coming be in peace, and your going forth.

Moderato

Sho - lom a - le - hem, mal - a - hey ha - sho - res, Mal - a - hey el - - -
Tzes - hem t' - sho - lom, mal - a - hey ha - sho - lom, Mal - a - hey el - - -

yon, ... mi - - me - leh mal - hey ham - to - him
yon, ... mi - - me - leh mal - hey ham - to - him

Slowly, religiously.

Sho — lom a — ley — hem mal — a — hey ha — sho — — res,......
Bo — a — hem l' — sho — lom mal — a — hey ha — sho — — lom,......

Mal — a — hey....... el — — yon, mi — me — leh mal — hey ham — lo —

him... Ha — ko — dosh bo — — ruh......

hu.......................... Ha — ko — dosh bo — ruh hu.........................

On the sixth day the heaven and the earth and all their hosts were finished. And the Lord rested on the seventh day and blessed it. Blessed art Thou, O Lord, who hast created the fruit of the vine and given us the Sabbath as a remembrance of the days of creation.

Slowly

Solo   Cong.
Bo — ruḥ a-to A-do-noi, Bo ruḥ hu u-vo-ruḥ sh'mo, e-lo-

-hey-nu me-leḥ ho-o-lom........... bo — rey........ p'-ri ha — go-fen.

Cong.   Solo   Cong.
o — — men. Bo — ruḥ a-to A-do noi, Bo-ruḥ hu u-vo-ruḥ sh'mo,

E-lo — hey-nu me-leḥ ho-o-lom..... a-sher ki-d'sho-nu b'-mitz-vo-sov v'-ro-

tzon vo-nu..... v'-sha — bas kod — — sho b'-a-ha-vo..... uv-ro-

tzon hin-ḥi-lo — — — nu zi-ko — ron l'-ma-a-sey v'-rey-shis...........

Ki hu vom t'-ḥi-lo l'-mik-ro — ey... ko — -desh zey-ḥer li-tzi-as mitz-ro-yim.

 בָּרוּךְ אַתָּה יְיָ אֱלֹהֵינוּ מֶלֶךְ הָעוֹלָם בּוֹרֵא פְּרִי הַגָּפֶן: בָּרוּךְ אַתָּה יְיָ אֱלֹהֵינוּ מֶלֶךְ
הָעוֹלָם אֲשֶׁר קִדְּשָׁנוּ בְּמִצְוֹתָיו וְרָצָה בָנוּ וְשַׁבַּת קָדְשׁוֹ בְּאַהֲבָה וּבְרָצוֹן הִנְחִילָנוּ זִכָּרוֹן
לְמַעֲשֵׂה בְרֵאשִׁית. כִּי הוּא יוֹם תְּחִלָּה לְמִקְרָאֵי קֹדֶשׁ זֵכֶר לִיצִיאַת מִצְרָיִם. כִּי בָנוּ
בָחַרְתָּ וְאוֹתָנוּ קִדַּשְׁתָּ מִכָּל הָעַמִּים וְשַׁבַּת קָדְשְׁךָ בְּאַהֲבָה וּבְרָצוֹן הִנְחַלְתָּנוּ, בָּרוּךְ
אַתָּה יְיָ מְקַדֵּשׁ הַשַּׁבָּת.

14

Z'mirot and Oneg Shabbat

HINEY MA TOV

*) ① Hi-ney ma tov u-ma na - - im.... She-vet a - him gam ya - - had.

② Hi - ney ma....... tov...... she-vet a - him gam ya - - had.......

Hi - ney...... ma - - tov she-vet a - him gam ya - had.

*) Round

How goodly it is and how pleasant for brethren to dwell together.

הִנֵּה מַה טּוֹב וּמַה נָּעִים שֶׁבֶת אַחִים
גַּם יָחַד.

15

N'RAN'NA

Let us sing and rejoice! Let us sing and rejoice!

YOM ZE L'YISROEL

Yom ze l'-Yis-ro-el Sha-bos m'-nu-ho, Sha-bos m'-nu-ho, Sha-bos m'-nu-ho.

Yom ze l'-Yis-ro-el Sha-bos m'-nu-ho, Sha-bos..... m'-nu-ho.

The Sabbath is a day of light and joy and rest to Israel.

יוֹם זֶה לְיִשְׂרָאֵל
שַׁבָּת מְנוּחָה.

V'TAHER LIBENU

V'-ta-her li-bey-nu l'-ov-d'-ho, l'-ov-d'-ho, l'-ov-d'-ho, l'-ov-d'-ho b'-

Oh, purify our hearts that we may worship Thee in truth.

וְטַהֵר לִבֵּנוּ לְעָבְדְּךָ בֶּאֱמֶת.

....ל, ל, ל

HIN'NI MUHON

*Behold, I am prepared to sanctify the Sabbath, as
is written in the Torah.*

U-k'dash-tem lo-hem es yom ha-sha-bos,...... Hi-n'-ni mu-hon u – m'zu — mon. U-

k'dash-tem lo-hem es yom ha-Sha-bos, ... Hi-n'-ni mù-hon u – m'zu—mon.

HIN'NI MUHON

מקהלה:

וְקִדַּשְׁתָּם לָכֶם אֶת יוֹם הַשַּׁבָּת,

הִנְנִי מוּכָן וּמְזֻמָּן.

הִנְנִי מוּכָן וּמְזֻמָּן,

כְּמוֹ שֶׁכָּתוּב בַּתּוֹרָה,

הִנְנִי מוּכָן וּמְזֻמָּן.

הִנְנִי ...

הִנְנִי ...

SHABBOS SHOLOM

Earnestly

Sha - bos sho-lom, sho - lom a-le-hem...... Mal - a - hey
Bo - - - a-hem .... l' - sho- lom ......

ha-sho-lom, mal-a-ḥey ha-sho-res, Mal-a-ḥey el-yon........ Mi-

me-leḥ mal-ḥey ha-m'-lo-him Ha-ko-dosh........ bo-ruḥ hu........

*) In the East, it's an accepted tradition to begin this song with "Shabbat Shalom"

Peace unto you, O angels of peace. May your
coming be in peace, and your going forth.

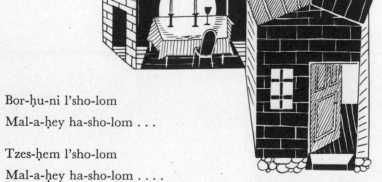

Bor-ḥu-ni l'sho-lom
Mal-a-ḥey ha-sho-lom . . .

Tzes-ḥem l'sho-lom
Mal-a-ḥey ha-sho-lom . . . .

שַׁבַּת שָׁלוֹם, שָׁלוֹם עֲלֵיכֶם,
מַלְאֲכֵי הַשָּׁלוֹם, מַלְאֲכֵי הַשָּׁרֵת,
מַלְאֲכֵי עֶלְיוֹן,
מִמֶּלֶךְ מַלְכֵי הַמְּלָכִים
הַקָּדוֹשׁ בָּרוּךְ הוּא.

בּוֹאֲכֶם לְשָׁלוֹם
מַלְאֲכֵי הַשָּׁלוֹם . . .

בָּרְכוּנִי לְשָׁלוֹם
מַלְאֲכֵי הַשָּׁלוֹם . . . .

צֵאתְכֶם לְשָׁלוֹם
מַלְאֲכֵי הַשָּׁלוֹם . . . .

21

ATO EḤOD

l'--am-ho no-sa--to,　Yom m'nu-ho u--k'du--sho.........　l'--am-ho no--sa--to.

Thou art one and Thy people Israel is one. Thou hast given Thy people a day of rest and sanctity.

אַתָּה אֶחָד וְשִׁמְךָ אֶחָד, מִי כְעַמְּךָ יִשְׂרָאֵל,
מִי כְעַמְּךָ יִשְׂרָאֵל, גּוֹי אֶחָד בָּאָרֶץ.
תִּפְאֶרֶת גְּדֻלָּה, וַעֲטֶרֶת יְשׁוּעָה.
יוֹם מְנוּחָה וּקְדוּשָׁה לְעַמְּךָ נָתָתָ.

SHIRU LADONOI

With grace

Shi--ru la--do--noi.........　Shi--ru shir ho--dosh.........

shi--ru shi--ru hol ho--o--retz, Shi--ru bor--hu sh--mo........　ru bor--hu sh--mo.

Sing a new song unto the Lord. Let all the world
sing and bless His name.

שִׁירוּ לַיְיָ, שִׁירוּ שִׁיר חָדָשׁ
שִׁירוּ, שִׁירוּ כָל הָאָרֶץ:
שִׁירוּ בָּרְכוּ שְׁמוֹ:
לַ, לַ, לַ ...

HASHIVENU ELEHO

With vigor

Ha-shi-vey-nu e-le-ho v'-no-shu-vo,...

ha-desh yo-mey-nu k'-ke-dem........ Ha-shi-vey-nu e--le-ho

v'-no-shu-vo.... ha-desh yo-mey-nu k'-ke-dem......

La la la la la

Restore us unto Thee and we shall be restored.
Renew our days as of yore.

BO'OLOM HABO

In the world to come a restful Sabbath awaits you. Heed not the pre-Messiah pains, for the son of David comes.

28

בְּעוֹלָם הַבָּא שַׁבָּת מְנוּחָה.
חֶבְלֵי מָשִׁיחַ, בֶּן דָּוִד בָּא.
לַ לַ לַ . . . . .

hev - ley   mo-shi - aḥ   ben Do-vid.. bo........   La, la, la,

29

M'NUḤO V'SIMḤO

Joyously

M'nu-ho v'-sim-ho,....... or la-y'hu-dim, Yom....... sha-bo-son, yom maḥ-ma-dim. Shom-rov v'-zoḥ-rov....

hey-mo m'-i-dim. Ki l'-shi-sho ḥol bru-im v'—om——dim.........

om—dim. .... Sh'mey sho-ma-yim, sh'mey sho-ma-yim e-retz v'-

ya-mim. Kol tz'vo mo-rom, kol tzvo mo-rom g'vo-him v'-ro — — mim.

Ta-nin v'-o-dom v'-ha-yas r'-e-mim. Ki v'yo A-do-noi tzur o-

lo — — mim...... lo - - - mim.

The Sabbath is a day of rest, joy and light for the Jews. Its observers will testify that all things were created in six days and that God alone is the Rock of Eternity.

מְנוּחָה וְשִׂמְחָה, אוֹר לַיְּהוּדִים.
יוֹם שַׁבָּתוֹן, יוֹם מַחֲמַדִּים.
שׁוֹמְרָיו וְזוֹכְרָיו הֵמָּה מְעִידִים.
כִּי לְשִׁשָּׁה כָּל בְּרוּאִים וְעוֹמְדִים.

שְׁמֵי שָׁמַיִם אֶרֶץ וְיַמִּים.
כָּל צְבָא מָרוֹם גְּבוֹהִים וְרָמִים.
תַּנִּין וְאָדָם וְחַיַּת רְאֵמִים.
כִּי בְּיָהּ יְיָ צוּר עוֹלָמִים.

YO RIBON OLOM

O God who created all things, King of kings, Thy praises shall I recount morning and night.

Sh'vo-ḥin a-sa-der tzaf-ro v'ram-sho,
Loḥ e-lo-ho di v'ro ḥol naf-sho
I-rin ka-di-shin uv'ney an-sho,
Ḥa-yos bo-ro v'o-fey sh'ma-yo.

יָהּ רִבּוֹן עָלַם וְעָלְמַיָּא,
אַנְתְּ הוּא מַלְכָּא מֶלֶךְ מַלְכַיָּא.
עוֹבַד גְּבוּרְתֵּךְ וְתִמְהַיָּא,
שְׁפַר קֳדָמָךְ לְהַחֲוָיָה.

שְׁבָחִין אֲסַדֵּר צַפְרָא וְרַמְשָׁא,
לָךְ אֱלָהָא דִּי בְרָא כָל נַפְשָׁא.
עִירִין קַדִּישִׁין וּבְנֵי אֱנָשָׁא,
חֵיוַת בָּרָא וְעוֹפֵי שְׁמַיָּא.

TZUR MISHELO

ROCK OF PLENTY

With devotion

Tzur mi-she-lo, mi-she-lo o-hal-nu bor-hu e-mu-
Rock of plen-ty, life to liv-ing, Bless-ings to Him

nai So-va-nu so-va-nu so-va-nu v'-ho-sar-nu kid-var A-do-
sing! Life and food all crea-tures giv-ing, Thou art Lord, our

noi Ha-zon es o-lo-mo ro-e-nu o-
King. Stores of plen-ty Thou dost bring, Gifts of bread and

34

vi - nu...... O - hal - nu es - tah - mo....... v'yey - no sho - si -
wine,.......... *Thou art shep - herd,* *fa - ther, King;*.... *All we have is*

nu. Al ken no - de lish - mo u - n'ha - l' - lo b' - fi - nu...... 'O -
Thine. *Sing, then, sing a song of praise..... God our Fa - ther, He is one ;.....*

mar - nu..... v' - o - ni - nu........... en ko - dosh ka - do - noi.......
Thank - ful'....... we our voi - ces raise,....... Like un - to Him... there is none.......

Tzur mi - she - lo mi - she - lo o - hal - nu bor - hu e - mu - nai...... So -
Rock of....... plen - ty,.... life to liv - ing, Bless - ings to Him sing!......

va-nu so-va-nu so-va-nu v'-ho-sar-nu kid-var A-do-noi.
Life and... food all.... crea - tures giv-ing; Thou art Lord, our King......

צוּר מִשֶּׁלּוֹ אָכַלְנוּ, בָּרְכוּ אֱמוּנַי.
שָׂבַעְנוּ וְהוֹתַרְנוּ כִּדְבַר יְיָ:

הַזָּן אֶת עוֹלָמוֹ, רוֹעֵנוּ אָבִינוּ.
אָכַלְנוּ אֶת לַחְמוֹ וְיֵינוֹ שָׁתִינוּ.

עַל כֵּן נוֹדֶה לִשְׁמוֹ וּנְהַלְלוֹ בְּפִינוּ.
אָמַרְנוּ וְעָנִינוּ, אֵין קָדוֹשׁ כַּיְיָ:
צוּר מִשֶּׁלּוֹ . . . .

SHIR HAMA'ALOS

'TWAS LIKE A DREAM

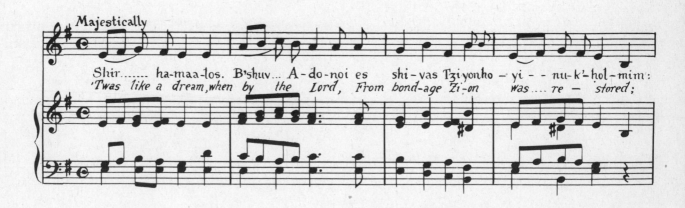

Majestically

Shir....... ha-maa-los. B'shuv... A-do-noi es shi-vas Tziyonho - yi - -nu-k'-hol-mim:
'Twas like a dream, when by the Lord, From bond-age Zi-on was.... re - stored;

D.S. % al Fine

Ha - - - - zor'-im b'- - - dim - o . . . . b'- ri-no yik - tzo-ru:
While go-ing forth, yet shall they sing When, coming back, their sheaves they bring.

שִׁיר הַמַּעֲלוֹת. בְּשׁוּב יְיָ אֶת שִׁיבַת צִיּוֹן הָיִינוּ כְּחֹלְמִים: אָז יִמָּלֵא שְׂחֹק פִּינוּ וּלְשׁוֹנֵנוּ
רִנָּה אָז יֹאמְרוּ בַגּוֹיִם הִגְדִּיל יְיָ לַעֲשׂוֹת עִם אֵלֶּה: הִגְדִּיל יְיָ לַעֲשׂוֹת עִמָּנוּ הָיִינוּ
שְׂמֵחִים: שׁוּבָה יְיָ אֶת שְׁבִיתֵנוּ כַּאֲפִיקִים בַּנֶּגֶב: הַזֹּרְעִים בְּדִמְעָה בְּרִנָּה יִקְצֹרוּ: הָלוֹךְ
יֵלֵךְ וּבָכֹה נֹשֵׂא מֶשֶׁךְ הַזָּרַע בֹּא יָבֹא בְרִנָּה נֹשֵׂא אֲלֻמֹּתָיו:

BIRKAS HAMOZON

Freely sung
SOLO   Group:

Ra-bo- sai n'-vo-reḥ: Y'-hi shem A-do-noi m'- vo- -roh me-a-

vi - nu mal — ke -nu adi — re -nu bor — e -nu go-a-

le — nu yotz — re — nu k'do — she — nu V'-nim-tzo

hen v'-se- hel tov b'e -ne Elo — him v'-o — dom. Mig-

dol y'shu-os........ mal - ko v'-o -se...... he-sed lim-shi — ho........ l'-

Do - vid u-l'-zar - o....... ad o - - tom: O - se sho-lom bim - ro - - mov

hu ya-a-se sho-lom o-ley-nu o-ley - nu v'al kol Yis-ro el v'-im-ru o - men.

רַבּוֹתַי נְבָרֵךְ:

יְהִי שֵׁם יְיָ מְבֹרָךְ מֵעַתָּה וְעַד עוֹלָם:

בִּרְשׁוּת רַבּוֹתַי נְבָרֵךְ (אֱלֹהֵינוּ) שֶׁאָכַלְנוּ מִשֶּׁלוֹ:

בָּרוּךְ (אֱלֹהֵינוּ) שֶׁאָכַלְנוּ מִשֶּׁלוֹ וּבְטוּבוֹ חָיִינוּ:

הוּא נוֹתֵן לֶחֶם לְכָל בָּשָׂר כִּי לְעוֹלָם חַסְדּוֹ:

בָּרוּךְ אַתָּה יְיָ הַזָּן אֶת הַכֹּל:

כַּכָּתוּב וְאָכַלְתָּ וְשָׂבָעְתָּ . . . בָּרוּךְ אַתָּה יְיָ עַל הָאָרֶץ וְעַל הַמָּזוֹן:

אֱלֹהֵינוּ אָבִינוּ רְעֵנוּ זוּנֵנוּ פַּרְנְסֵנוּ וְכַלְכְּלֵנוּ וְהַרְוִיחֵנוּ . . .

שֶׁלֹא נֵבוֹשׁ וְלֹא נִכָּלֵם לְעוֹלָם וָעֶד . . . בְּנֵה בְרַחֲמָיו יְרוּשָׁלָיִם . . .

הָאֵל אָבִינוּ מַלְכֵּנוּ אַדִּירֵנוּ בּוֹרְאֵנוּ גֹּאֲלֵנוּ יוֹצְרֵנוּ קְדוֹשֵׁנוּ . . .

וְנִמְצָא חֵן וְשֵׂכֶל טוֹב בְּעֵינֵי אֱלֹהִים וְאָדָם . . .

מִגְדּוֹל יְשׁוּעוֹת מַלְכּוֹ וְעֹשֶׂה חֶסֶד לִמְשִׁיחוֹ לְדָוִד וּלְזַרְעוֹ עַד עוֹלָם:

עֹשֶׂה שָׁלוֹם בִּמְרוֹמָיו הוּא יַעֲשֶׂה שָׁלוֹם עָלֵינוּ וְעַל כָּל יִשְׂרָאֵל וְאִמְרוּ אָמֵן.

May the name of the Lord be blessed forever. He provides bread for all, for His mercy is
everlasting. He shall bring peace upon us and upon all Israel, Amen.

L'ḤO DODI

Moderato

L' — ḥo do - di.... lik - ras ka - lo, P' - ney Sha - bos... n' - ka - b - lo.

Come, my beloved, let us go forth to meet the
Sabbath bride.

לְכָה דוֹדִי לִקְרַאת כַּלָּה, פְּנֵי שַׁבָּת
נְקַבְּלָה:

Moderately

L'ḥo do — — di lik - ras ka — — lo, P' — ne sha —

bos n' - kab — — — lo:..... bos n' - ka — — b' - lo:.....

* *Can be sung as a round.*

BO'I V'SHOLOM

Come in peace, O Sabbath, crown of Israel. Come
amongst those who believe, with joyous dance. Come,
O Sabbath bride.

בֹּאִי בְשָׁלוֹם עֲטֶרֶת בַּעְלָה.
גַּם בְּשִׂמְחָה וּבְצָהֳלָה.
תּוֹךְ אֱמוּנֵי עַם סְגֻלָה:
בֹּאִי כַלָּה, בֹּאִי כַלָּה:
לְכָה דוֹדִי . . .

AHAVAS OLOM

Slowly

A - ha-vas o - lom.... bes Yis-ro - el am-ho o-hov - to........ To-

roh.... u - mitz - vos....... to - roh u-mitz-vos ḥu - kim u-mish-po-tim o-

so-nu li-mad'-to.... Al ken A-do-noi E-lo-hey-nu b'-shoh-

ve-nu uv---ku-mey-nu no-si-ah b'-hu-ke-ho........ V'-nis-

mah b'-div-rey so-ro-se—ho...... uv-mitz-vo-se-ho l'o-tom vo--ed......

Thou hast loved Thy people Israel with an everlasting love and hast taught us Thy laws and Thy commandments. Therefore shall we rejoice in Thy Torah forever.

אַהֲבַת עוֹלָם בֵּית יִשְׂרָאֵל עַמְּךָ
אָהָבְתָּ. תּוֹרָה וּמִצְוֹת חֻקִּים
וּמִשְׁפָּטִים אוֹתָנוּ לִמַּדְתָּ. עַל כֵּן יְיָ
אֱלֹהֵינוּ בְּשָׁכְבֵנוּ וּבְקוּמֵנוּ נָשִׂיחַ
בְּחֻקֶּיךָ. וְנִשְׂמַח בְּדִבְרֵי תוֹרָתֶךָ
וּבְמִצְוֹתֶיךָ לְעוֹלָם וָעֶד.

Hear, O Israel, the Lord our God, the Lord is One.

שְׁמַע יִשְׂרָאֵל, יְיָ אֱלֹהֵינוּ, יְיָ אֶחָד.

MI ḤOMOḤO

ro   s'-hi - los   o - se................ fe - le

A - do - noi   yim - loh   l' - o - lom...... vo - ed.

Who is like Thee among the gods, O Lord.

Who like Thee is glorified in holiness.

The Lord shall reign forever.

מִי־כָמֹכָה בָּאֵלִים יְיָ,

מִי כָּמֹכָה נֶאְדָּר בַּקֹּדֶשׁ,

נוֹרָא תְהִלֹת, עֹשֵׂה פֶלֶא:

יְיָ יִמְלֹךְ לְעוֹלָם וָעֶד.

es ha-sho-ma-yim v' - es ho-o-retz,.... U-va-yom... hash'-vi-i........

sho-vas.... va-yi-no-fash,.... va-yi-no-fash:...

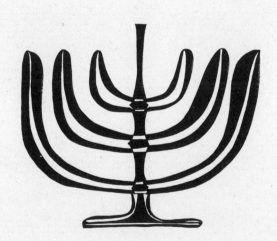

וְשָׁמְרוּ בְנֵי־יִשְׂרָאֵל אֶת־הַשַּׁבָּת.
לַעֲשׂוֹת אֶת הַשַּׁבָּת לְדֹרֹתָם, בְּרִית
עוֹלָם:
בֵּינִי וּבֵין בְּנֵי־יִשְׂרָאֵל אוֹת הִיא
לְעֹלָם,
כִּי־שֵׁשֶׁת יָמִים עָשָׂה יְיָ אֶת־הַשָּׁמַיִם
וְאֶת־הָאָרֶץ,
וּבַיּוֹם הַשְּׁבִיעִי שָׁבַת וַיִּנָּפַשׁ:

Israel shall keep the Sabbath. It is a sign between
Me and Israel forever. For in six days the Lord
made the heaven and the earth, and on the Sabbath
He rested.

The heaven and the earth and all their hosts were *finished, and the Lord rested on the seventh day and* *blessed it.*

וַיְכֻלּוּ הַשָּׁמַיִם וְהָאָרֶץ וְכָל־צְבָאָם:
וַיְכַל אֱלֹהִים בַּיּוֹם הַשְּׁבִיעִי
מְלַאכְתּוֹ אֲשֶׁר עָשָׂה.
וַיִּשְׁבֹּת בַּיּוֹם הַשְּׁבִיעִי מִכָּל־
מְלַאכְתּוֹ אֲשֶׁר עָשָׂה:
וַיְבָרֶךְ אֱלֹהִים אֶת יוֹם הַשְּׁבִיעִי
וַיְקַדֵּשׁ אֹתוֹ,
כִּי בוֹ שָׁבַת מִכָּל מְלַאכְתּוֹ, אֲשֶׁר
בָּרָא אֱלֹהִים לַעֲשׂוֹת:

MOGEN OVOS

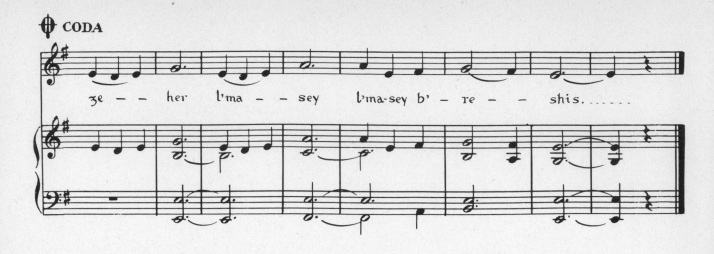

ze — — her l'ma — — sey   l'ma-sey b' — re — — shis.......

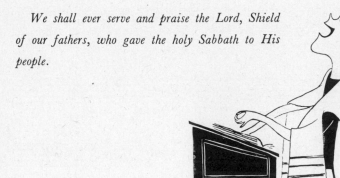

We shall ever serve and praise the Lord, Shield of our fathers, who gave the holy Sabbath to His people.

מָגֵן אָבוֹת בִּדְבָרוֹ, מְחַיֶּה מֵתִים
בְּמַאֲמָרוֹ, הָאֵל הַקָּדוֹשׁ שֶׁאֵין
כָּמוֹהוּ, הַמֵּנִיחַ לְעַמּוֹ בְּיוֹם שַׁבַּת
קָדְשׁוֹ, כִּי בָם רָצָה לְהָנִיחַ לָהֶם.
לְפָנָיו נַעֲבוֹד בְּיִרְאָה וָפַחַד וְנוֹדֶה
לִשְׁמוֹ בְּכָל יוֹם תָּמִיד מֵעֵין
הַבְּרָכוֹת. אֵל הַהוֹדָאוֹת אֲדוֹן
הַשָּׁלוֹם מְקַדֵּשׁ הַשַּׁבָּת וּמְבָרֵךְ
שְׁבִיעִי וּמֵנִיחַ בִּקְדֻשָּׁה לְעַם מְדֻשְּׁנֵי
עֹנֶג, זֵכֶר לְמַעֲשֵׂה בְרֵאשִׁית.

YIGDAL

May the Lord be glorified and praised. He is the Lord of the universe. He is One, without form and everlasting.

Moderato

Yig-dal.....E-lo-him..... hai v'-yish-ta — — bah.......nim-

tzo .... v' — eyn .... eys .... el m'—tzi—o — so ....

E — ḥod .... v' — en yo—hid k' yi — — — — hu — — do .... ne—

lom .... v' — gam en sof ..... l' — ah — — — du — so ....

En lo d'mus ha-guf, v'e-no guf;	אֵין לוֹ דְּמוּת הַגּוּף, וְאֵינוֹ גוּף;	יִגְדַּל אֱלֹהִים חַי, וְיִשְׁתַּבַּח;
lo na-a-roḫ e-lov k'du-sho-so:	לֹא נַעֲרוֹךְ אֵלָיו קְדֻשָּׁתוֹ:	נִמְצָא, וְאֵין עֵת אֶל-מְצִיאוּתוֹ:
Kad-mon l'ḥol do-vor a-sher niv-ro;	קַדְמוֹן לְכָל-דָּבָר אֲשֶׁר נִבְרָא;	אֶחָד, וְאֵין יָחִיד כְּיִחוּדוֹ;
ri-shon, v'en re-shis l're-shi-so:	רִאשׁוֹן, וְאֵין רֵאשִׁית לְרֵאשִׁיתוֹ:	נֶעְלָם, וְגַם אֵין סוֹף לְאַחְדּוּתוֹ:
Hi-no a-don o-lom l'ḥol no-tzor;	הִנּוֹ אֲדוֹן עוֹלָם לְכָל-נוֹצָר;	
yo-re g'du-lo-so u-mal-hu-so:	יוֹרֶה גְדֻלָּתוֹ וּמַלְכוּתוֹ:	
She-fa n'vu-o-so n'so-no;	שֶׁפַע נְבוּאָתוֹ נְתָנוֹ;	
El an-shey s'gu-lo-so v'sif-ar-to:	אֶל אַנְשֵׁי סְגֻלָּתוֹ וְתִפְאַרְתּוֹ:	

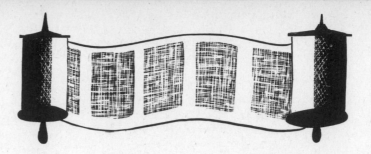

MA TOVU

How goodly are your tents, O Jacob, your tabernacles, O Israel. O Lord, I love the place where Thy glory dwells. I shall bow before the Lord, my Creator. Answer me, O Lord, for my prayer is before Thee.

In a dignified manner, but not too slowly.

Ma to-vu o-ho-le-ho Ya-a-kov........ mish-k'no-se-ho Yis-ro-el......

Va-a-ni b'rov has-d'-ho,..... o--vo ve-se---ho, esh-ta-ha-

ve..... el he-hal, el he-hal kod-sh' ho.... b'-yir-o-se---ho: A-do-

noi o-hav-ti m'-on .. be - se-ḥo um'-kom mish-kan k'-vo - -de-ḥo.

Solo

Va - a - ni esh - ta-ḥa-ve.... v' - eḥ - ro - - o...... ev' - r' - ḥo.........

ev' - r' - ḥo.........lif - ney Ado-noi o - si..... Va - a - ni s'-fi-lo-si l'-

ḥo Ado - noi.........es...... ro - - - tzon,.... e - lo - him b'rov

has-de-ho......a - ne-ni bee-me-syish-e - - ho........... a - ne-ni bee-me-syish-e - - ho.....

מַה טֹּבוּ אֹהָלֶיךָ יַעֲקֹב, מִשְׁכְּנֹתֶיךָ
יִשְׂרָאֵל. וַאֲנִי בְּרֹב חַסְדְּךָ, אָבֹא
בֵיתֶךָ, אֶשְׁתַּחֲוֶה אֶל הֵיכַל קָדְשְׁךָ
בְּיִרְאָתֶךָ. יְיָ אָהַבְתִּי מְעוֹן בֵּיתֶךָ,

וּמְקוֹם מִשְׁכַּן כְּבוֹדֶךָ. וַאֲנִי אֶשְׁתַּחֲוֶה
וְאֶכְרָעָה אֶבְרְכָה לִפְנֵי יְיָ עֹשִׂי.
וַאֲנִי תְפִלָּתִי לְךָ יְיָ עֵת רָצוֹן, אֱלֹהִים
בְּרָב חַסְדֶּךָ עֲנֵנִי בֶּאֱמֶת יִשְׁעֶךָ.

KODOSH

Majestically

Ko - dosh, ko - dosh, ko - dosh A - do - noi tz'-vo-

os...... M'lo ḥol ho - o - retz k'vo - - do.......

Holy, holy, holy is the Lord of Hosts. All the earth is filled with His glory.

Blessed be the glory of the Lord from His place.

The Lord shall reign forever; Thy God, O Zion, shall be Sovereign unto all generations. Hallelujah.

קָדוֹשׁ, קָדוֹשׁ, קָדוֹשׁ יְיָ צְבָאוֹת.
מְלֹא כָל הָאָרֶץ כְּבוֹדוֹ:

בָּרוּךְ כְּבוֹד יְיָ מִמְּקוֹמוֹ:

יִמְלֹךְ ה' לְעוֹלָם. אֱלֹהַיִךְ צִיּוֹן
לְדֹר וָדֹר. הַלְלוּיָהּ:

YISMAH MOSHE

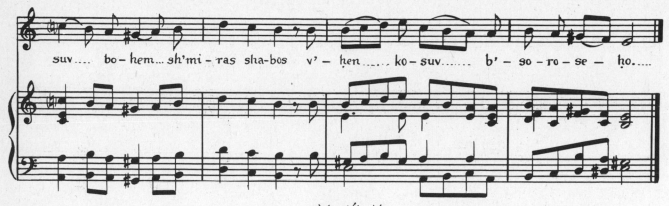

suv.... bo-hem.... sh'mi-ras sha-bos v'-hen.... ko-suv....... b'- so-ro-se — ho.....

Let Moses rejoice in his portion, for Thou didst call him Thy faithful servant when he stood before Thee on Mount Sinai. Upon the tablets he brought down was engraved the commandment to observe the Sabbath.

יִשְׂמַח מֹשֶׁה בְּמַתְּנַת חֶלְקוֹ. כִּי עֶבֶד נֶאֱמָן קָרָאתָ לּוֹ. כְּלִיל תִּפְאֶרֶת בְּרֹאשׁוֹ נָתָתָּ. בְּעָמְדוֹ לְפָנֶיךָ עַל הַר־סִינַי. וּשְׁנֵי לוּחוֹת אֲבָנִים הוֹרִיד בְּיָדוֹ. וְכָתוּב בָּהֶם שְׁמִירַת שַׁבָּת. וְכֵן כָּתוּב בְּתוֹרָתֶךָ:

AV HORAḤAMIM

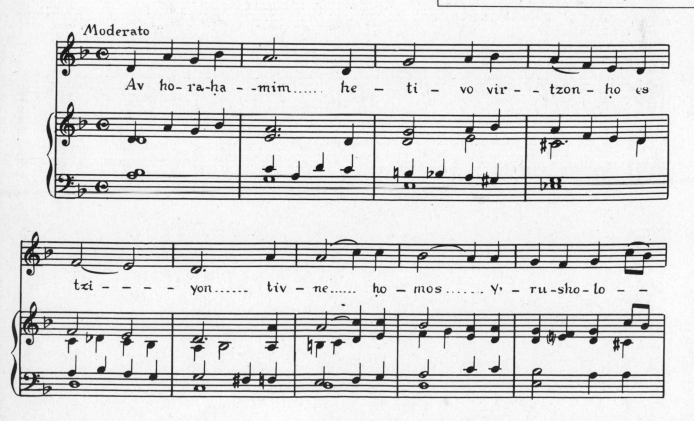

Moderato

Av ho-ra-ha-mim...... he - ti - vo vir-tzon-ho es

tzi - - - - yon...... tiv-ne...... ho-mos...... Y - ru-sho-lo -

Father of mercy, build up the walls of Jerusalem,
for our faith is in Thee, O Lord of the universe.

אַב הָרַחֲמִים הֵיטִיבָה בִרְצוֹנְךָ אֶת
צִיּוֹן,
תִּבְנֶה חוֹמוֹת יְרוּשָׁלָיִם: כִּי בְךָ לְבַד
בָּטָחְנוּ, מֶלֶךְ אֵל רָם וְנִשָּׂא אֲדוֹן
עוֹלָמִים:

Majestically

1. Ki mi-Tzi — yon te-tze..... so-ro.... Ki mi-Tzi — yon.... te-
2. Bo-ruḥ she-no-san to-roh.... to-roh.... Bo-ruḥ she-no-san..... to-

tze..... so-ro,.. Ud'— —var A-do— noi mi-Y'ru-sho-lo— —yim.
roh...... to-roh, L'-a-mo Yis-ro-el bik'—du-sho— —so.

The Torah shall come forth out of Zion, and the word of the Lord from Jerusalem.

Blessed be He who in His holiness gave the Torah unto His people Israel.

כִּי מִצִּיּוֹן תֵּצֵא תוֹרָה,
וּדְבַר יְיָ מִירוּשָׁלָיִם.

בָּרוּךְ שֶׁנָּתַן תּוֹרָה,
לְעַמּוֹ יִשְׂרָאֵל בִּקְדוּשָׁתוֹ.

SH'MA YISROEL

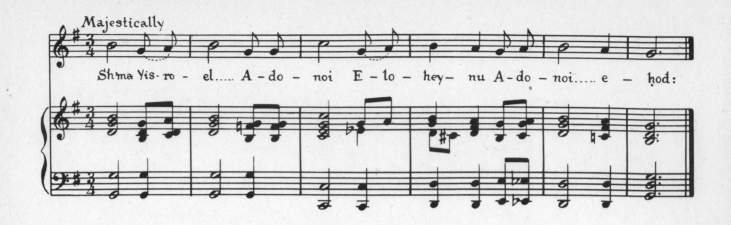

Majestically

Sh'ma Yis-ro - el..... A-do-noi E-lo-hey-nu A-do-noi..... e - hod:

Slowly

E-hodE-lo - hey-nu go - dol A-do - ne-nu ko - dosh..... shimo.

Hear, O Israel, the Lord our God, the Lord is One.

Blessed be His name forever.

שְׁמַע יִשְׂרָאֵל יְיָ אֱלֹהֵינוּ יְיָ אֶחָד:

אֶחָד אֱלֹהֵינוּ, נָדוֹל אֲדוֹנֵינוּ, קָדוֹשׁ שְׁמוֹ.

64

L'HO ADONOI

Thine, O Lord, is the grandeur and the might
and the glory. All that is in the heavens and on the
earth is Thine, O Lord.

לְךָ אֲדֹנָי הַגְּדֻלָּה, וְהַגְּבוּרָה,
וְהַתִּפְאֶרֶת, וְהַנֵּצַח וְהַהוֹד
כִּי כֹל בַּשָּׁמַיִם וּבָאָרֶץ,
כִּי כֹל בַּשָּׁמַיִם וּבָאָרֶץ
לְךָ אֲדֹנָי הַמַּמְלָכָה
וְהַמִּתְנַשֵּׂא לְכֹל לְרֹאשׁ.

HODO AL ERETZ

Ho-do al e - -retz v'-sho - - ma-yim: Va-yo-rem ke - - ren t'-a-

mo t'-hi - - lo............ l'-hol hasi - dov........ liv-ney Yisro - el...... am k'-ro-

vo.. ha-la-lu — yo,...... ha-la-lu — yo, ha-la-lu — yo,...... ha-la-lu — yo:

His glory is on earth and in the heavens. He has raised the glory of His people, His righteous ones, the Children of Israel.

הוֹדוֹ עַל אֶרֶץ וְשָׁמָיִם: וַיָּרֶם קֶרֶן
לְעַמּוֹ
תְּהִלָּה לְכָל חֲסִידָיו לִבְנֵי יִשְׂרָאֵל
עַם קְרוֹבוֹ הַלְלוּיָהּ:

ETZ HAYIM HI

Slowly

Etz ha — yim...... hi la-ma-ha-zi-kim bo v'-so — m'-he-ho m'-u - - shor D'ro-

he - - ho..... dar - he no - am v' - hol n'-si-vo-se-ho sho - - lom Ha-
shi - - ve - nu A - - do - - - noi e - - le-ho v'no-shu - - vo ha-
desh..... yo-me-nu k' - ke - - dem ha - desh yo-me-nu k' - ke - - dem.

It is a Tree of Life to them that hold fast to it,
And everyone that upholds it is happy.
Its ways are ways of pleasantness,
And all its paths are peace.
Turn us unto Thee, O Lord, and we shall
    return;
Renew our days as of old.

עֵץ חַיִּים הִיא לַמַּחֲזִיקִים בָּהּ
וְתֹמְכֶיהָ מְאֻשָּׁר:
דְּרָכֶיהָ דַרְכֵי נֹעַם וְכָל נְתִיבוֹתֶיהָ
שָׁלוֹם:
הֲשִׁיבֵנוּ אֲדֹנָי אֵלֶיךָ וְנָשׁוּבָה
חַדֵּשׁ יָמֵינוּ כְּקֶדֶם.

KADSHENU

Sanctify us, O Lord, with Thy commandments.
Purify our hearts that we may worship Thee in
truth. Blessed art Thou who sanctifies the Sabbath.

קַדְּשֵׁנוּ בְּמִצְוֹתֶיךָ, וְתֵן חֶלְקֵנוּ
בְּתוֹרָתֶךָ.
שַׂבְּעֵנוּ מִטּוּבֶךָ, וְשַׂמְּחֵנוּ בִּישׁוּעָתֶךָ.
וְטַהֵר לִבֵּנוּ לְעָבְדְּךָ בֶּאֱמֶת,
וְהַנְחִילֵנוּ יְיָ אֱלֹהֵינוּ בְּאַהֲבָה וּבְרָצוֹן
שַׁבַּת קָדְשֶׁךָ
וְיָנוּחוּ בוֹ יִשְׂרָאֵל מְקַדְּשֵׁי שְׁמֶךָ.
בָּרוּךְ אַתָּה יְיָ, מְקַדֵּשׁ הַשַּׁבָּת.

70

SIM SHOLOM

Slowly

Sim, sim, sim sho-lom........ to - vo.... uv-ro-ho...... Hen, hen, hen vo-he-sed

he-sed v'ra-ha-mim. O - le - - - nu v'al kol Yis-ro-el, Yis-ro - el a-me-ho. Bor-

he - - - nu o-vi - nu, Ku-to-nu k'e - hod B'or po-ne - ho Ki

v'-or,........ v' - or po - ne-ho, v'-or,........ v' - or po-ne-ho,

Grant peace, blessing and mercy to us and all Israel. Bless us, O our Father, with the light of Thy countenance.

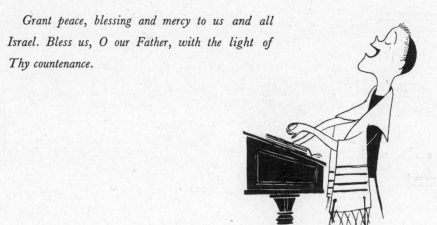

שִׂים שָׁלוֹם
טוֹבָה וּבְרָכָה,
חֵן וָחֶסֶד,
חֶסֶד וְרַחֲמִים
עָלֵינוּ וְעַל כָּל יִשְׂרָאֵל,
יִשְׂרָאֵל עַמֶּךָ.
בָּרְכֵנוּ אָבִינוּ
כֻּלָּנוּ כְּאֶחָד
בְּאוֹר פָּנֶיךָ.
כִּי בְאוֹר, בְּאוֹר פָּנֶיךָ,
בְּאוֹר, בְּאוֹר פָּנֶיךָ
נָתַתָּ לָנוּ תּוֹרַת חַיִּים.

EN KELOHENU

73

En..... k'-mal-ke-nu, En..... k'mo-shi-e-nu. Mi ..... he-lo-he-nu,
No-de l'-mal-ke-nu, No-de l'mo-shi-e-nu. Bo-ruḥ e-lo-he-nu,

Mi ..... ha-do-ne-nu, Mi ..... h'-mal-ke-nu, Mi h'mo-shi-e-nu.
Bo-ruḥ a-do-ne-nu, Bo-ruḥ mal-ke-nu, Bo-ruḥ mo-shi-e-nu.

There is no one like unto the Lord, our God. Let
us therefore thank Him, our King and Savior.

אֵין כֵּאלֹהֵינוּ. אֵין כַּאדוֹנֵינוּ:
אֵין כְּמַלְכֵּנוּ. אֵין כְּמוֹשִׁיעֵנוּ:

מִי כֵאלֹהֵינוּ. מִי כַאדוֹנֵינוּ:
מִי כְמַלְכֵּנוּ. מִי כְמוֹשִׁיעֵנוּ:

נוֹדֶה לֵאלֹהֵינוּ. נוֹדֶה לַאדוֹנֵינוּ:
נוֹדֶה לְמַלְכֵּנוּ. נוֹדֶה לְמוֹשִׁיעֵנוּ:

בָּרוּךְ אֱלֹהֵינוּ. בָּרוּךְ אֲדוֹנֵינוּ:
בָּרוּךְ מַלְכֵּנוּ. בָּרוּךְ מוֹשִׁיעֵנוּ:

A-to hu e-lo-hey-nu: A-to hu a-do-ne-nu:
A-to hu mal-ke-nu. A-to hu mo-shi-e-nu:

אַתָּה הוּא אֱלֹהֵינוּ. אַתָּה הוּא אֲדוֹנֵינוּ:
אַתָּה הוּא מַלְכֵּנוּ. אַתָּה הוּא מוֹשִׁיעֵנוּ:

ADON OLOM

A - don .... o - - lom .... a - sher .... mo - loh .... b'-

te-rem kol .... y' - - tzir .... niv-

Chorus

ro .... L' - es .... na - - so .... b' - - hef - - - tzo ....

kol .... a - zai .... me - - teh .... sh' - mo .... nik - - ro.

75

Moderato

A - don o - lom a - sher mo - lah b' - te - rem kol.... y' - tzir niv - ro
V' - a - ha - re ki - h'los ha - kol l' - va - do yim - loh.... no - ro

l'es na - a - so...... b' - hef - tzo kol a - zai me - leh sh' - mo nik - ro.
v'hu ho - - yo...... v' - hu ho - ve..... v' - hu yih - ye b' - sif - o - ro.

אֲדוֹן עוֹלָם אֲשֶׁר מָלַךְ
בְּטֶרֶם כָּל יְצִיר נִבְרָא:
לְעֵת נַעֲשָׂה בְחֶפְצוֹ כֹּל
אֲזַי מֶלֶךְ שְׁמוֹ נִקְרָא:
וְאַחֲרֵי כִּכְלוֹת הַכֹּל
לְבַדּוֹ יִמְלוֹךְ נוֹרָא:
וְהוּא הָיָה וְהוּא הֹוֶה
וְהוּא יִהְיֶה בְּתִפְאָרָה:

*Lord of the universe who ruled before anything
was created, who brought forth all creation at His
will. He was, He is, and He shall continue in glory.*

76

Blessed art Thou, O Lord, who created the fruit of the vine, who separated the holy from the profane, the Sabbath from all the other days of the week.

Bo - ruḥ a - to A - do - noi, Bo-ruḥ hu u-vo-ruḥ sh'-mo,

E - lo - hey-nu me-leḥ ho - o - lom,
{ Bo - rey...... p' - ri.... ha - go - fen.
  Bo - rey...... mi - ney.... v'so - mim.
  Bo - rey...... m'o - rey.... ho - esh. }
o - men. Bo - - ruḥ a - toh A - do - noi, Bo - ruḥ

hu u-vo-ruḥ sh'-mo, E - lo - hey-nu me-leḥ ho - o - lom, Ha-mav-

dil ben ko-desh t'-hol, ben or t'-ho-sheḥ, ben Yis-ro-el loa-mim, ben

yom ha-sh'vi - i t'- she-shes y'-mey ha-ma-a-seh. Bo-ruḥ a-toh A-do-noi,

Bo-ruḥ hu u-vo-ruḥ sh'-mo, Ha-mav - dil ben ko-desh t'-hol. O - men.

בָּרוּךְ אַתָּה יְיָ אֱלֹהֵינוּ מֶלֶךְ הָעוֹלָם, בּוֹרֵא פְּרִי הַגָּפֶן:
בָּרוּךְ אַתָּה יְיָ אֱלֹהֵינוּ מֶלֶךְ הָעוֹלָם, בּוֹרֵא מִינֵי בְשָׂמִים:
בָּרוּךְ אַתָּה יְיָ אֱלֹהֵינוּ מֶלֶךְ הָעוֹלָם, בּוֹרֵא מְאוֹרֵי הָאֵשׁ:
בָּרוּךְ אַתָּה יְיָ אֱלֹהֵינוּ מֶלֶךְ הָעוֹלָם, הַמַּבְדִּיל בֵּין קֹדֶשׁ לְחוֹל, בֵּין אוֹר לְחֹשֶׁךְ, בֵּין
יִשְׂרָאֵל לָעַמִּים, בֵּין יוֹם הַשְּׁבִיעִי לְשֵׁשֶׁת יְמֵי הַמַּעֲשֶׂה. בָּרוּךְ אַתָּה יְיָ הַמַּבְדִּיל בֵּין קֹדֶשׁ לְחוֹל:

HAMAVDIL

O GIVER OF SABBATH

tov,...... sho-vu-a tov,...... sho-vu-a tov,..... sho-vu-a tov......

הַמַּבְדִּיל בֵּין קֹדֶשׁ לְחוֹל,
חַטֹּאתֵינוּ הוּא יִמְחוֹל,
זַרְעֵנוּ וְכַסְפֵּנוּ יַרְבֶּה כַּחוֹל
וְכַכּוֹכָבִים בַּלָּיְלָה.
שָׁבוּעַ טוֹב . . . .

Yom po-no ḥ'tzel to-mer,
Ek-ro lo-El o-lai go-mer,
O-mar sho-mer, o-so vo-ker,
O-so vo-ker, v'gam loi-lo.
                    Sho-vu-a tov . . . .

יוֹם פָּנָה כְּצֵל תֹּמֶר,
אֶקְרָא לָאֵל עָלַי גֹּמֵר,
אָמַר שׁוֹמֵר, אָתָא בֹקֶר,
אָתָא בֹקֶר, וְגַם לָיְלָה.
שָׁבוּעַ טוֹב . . . .

O Giver of Sabbath, of Sabbath and peace,
May our sins and suffering cease,
As the stars in the heavens
May our days increase,
As the shining sands upon the shore.

CHORUS
*Sha-vu-a Tov (8)
Lord who weighs our deeds and ways
And sets apart our Holy Days,
Our sins forgive, may we succeed
To wealth and health and goodly seed.

The day is fled, the shadows spread,
And night comes on with stealthy tread.
The stars are out, now here's the moon,
Alas, the Sabbath's fled too soon.

The new week's here; come greet with cheer
Each dawning day; let's banish fear.
May this week see the world stay free
When man to man shall brother be.

CHORUS:
*or: A good week, a week of peace
     May gladness reign and joy increase.

SHAVU'A TOV

La, la, la,........

sha‒vu‒a tov, sha‒vu‒a tov.   sha‒vu‒a tov, sha‒vu‒a tov.

שָׁבוּעַ טוֹב

MOTZA'EY SHABBAT

OUTGOING SABBATH

Ha‒El,..... El Av‒‒ra‒ham, El
Oh, God of Abra‒ham hear‒‒ken, send

Ki ta-vo hab'ra-ḥa

B'ma-a-sey ya-de-nu,

V'lo ni-ga l'to-hu,

Lo nif-al la-shav.

Hoi, par-nes o-ta-nu

B'yo-sher uv'tze-dek.

Ul'to-ra ul'mitz-va

N'ga-del ha-taf . . .

כִּי תָבֹא הַבְּרָכָה

בְּמַעֲשֵׂה יָדֵינוּ,

וְלֹא נִיגַע לְתֹהוּ,

לֹא נִפְעַל לַשָּׁוְא.

הוֹי, פַּרְנֵס אוֹתָנוּ

בְּיֹשֶׁר וּבְצֶדֶק.

וּלְתוֹרָה וּלְמִצְוָה

נְגַדֵּל הַטָּף . . .

הָאֵל, אֵל אַבְרָהָם,

אֵל יִצְחָק וְיַעֲקֹב.

בְּצֵאת יוֹם הַשַּׁבָּת –

בַּשָּׁעָה הַזֹּאת

תְּכַנֵּס תְּפִלָּתִי

לִמְעוֹן הַשָּׁמָיִם, –

עֲשֵׂה נָא עִמָּנוּ

בְּחַסְדְּךָ אוֹת.

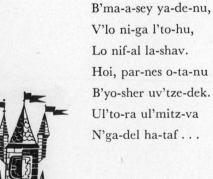

M'LAVE MALKA

L'SHONO TOVO

Slowly

L'-sho—no to-vo ti-ko-se-vu, l'-sho-no to-vo ti-ko-se—vu, ti-ko—se——vu v'-si-ho-se——mu.

לְשָׁנָה טוֹבָה תִּכָּתֵבוּ וְתֵחָתֵמוּ.

SH'MA YISROEL

Sh'ma yis-ro — el...... Ado — noi e-lo — — hey-nu Ado — noi.... e — hod.
E-hod e-lo — — hey-nu go-dol a-do — — ney-nu ko-dosh v'no-ro sh'mo.

שְׁמַע יִשְׂרָאֵל, יְיָ אֱלֹהֵינוּ, יְיָ אֶחָד:

Hear, O Israel, the Lord our God, the Lord is One.

אֶחָד אֱלֹהֵינוּ, גָּדוֹל אֲדוֹנֵינוּ, קָדוֹשׁ
וְנוֹרָא שְׁמוֹ.

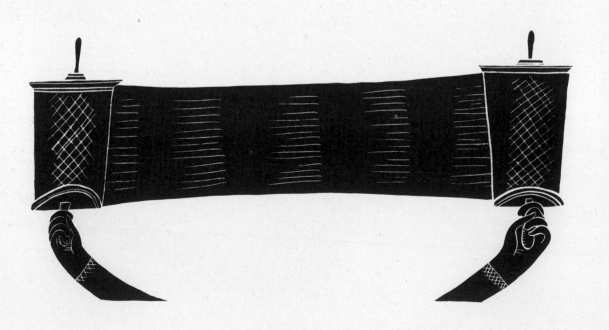

Remember us for life, O living God, and inscribe
us in the Book of Life.

זָכְרֵנוּ לְחַיִּים. מֶלֶךְ, חָפֵץ בַּחַיִּים.
וְכָתְבֵנוּ בְּסֵפֶר הַחַיִּים.
לְמַעַנְךָ, אֱלֹהִים חַיִּים.

OVINU MALKENU

Cantor then Cong.

O - vi - - - - nu............ mal - ke - nu......

ba - - - tel........ me-o-le - nu kol g'ze - ros ko - - - shos.
ba - - - tel........ mah - - sh'-vos...... so - - - ne - - - nu.

אָבִינוּ מַלְכֵּנוּ, חָטָאנוּ לְפָנֶיךָ:

אָבִינוּ מַלְכֵּנוּ, אֵין לָנוּ מֶלֶךְ אֶלָא
אָתָּה:

אָבִינוּ מַלְכֵּנוּ, עֲשֵׂה עִמָּנוּ לְמַעַן
שְׁמֶךָ:

אָבִינוּ מַלְכֵּנוּ, חַדֵּשׁ עָלֵינוּ שָׁנָה
טוֹבָה:

אָבִינוּ מַלְכֵּנוּ, בַּטֵּל מֵעָלֵינוּ כָּל
גְּזֵרוֹת קָשׁוֹת:

אָבִינוּ מַלְכֵּנוּ, בַּטֵּל מַחְשְׁבוֹת
שׂוֹנְאֵינוּ:

Our Father, our King, we have sinned before Thee. For the sake of Thy name, forgive us our sins, and grant us a good year.

UN'SANE TOKEF

Slowly

U - n'-sa - ne to - kef k'du-shas ha - yom ki hu........ no - ro v'o-

yom............ u - vo si-no-se mal-ḥu-se - ḥo...... v'yi - kon .... b'-

ḥe - sed kis - e - ḥo..... v' - se-shev o - lov.... bey - e - - mes.

*We observe the holiness of this day of awe,
when Thy dominion is exalted, and Thou dost sit
upon Thy throne in truth.*

וּנְתַנֶּה תּוֹקֶף קְדוּשַׁת הַיּוֹם, כִּי הוּא
נוֹרָא וְאָיוֹם, וּבוֹ תִנָּשֵׂא מַלְכוּתֶךָ,
וְיִכּוֹן בְּחֶסֶד כִּסְאֶךָ, וְתֵשֵׁב עָלָיו
בֶּאֱמֶת.

KOL NIDRE

כָּל נְדְרֵי וֶאֱסָרֵי וּשְׁבוּעֵי וַחֲרָמֵי
וְקוֹנָמֵי וְקִנּוּסֵי וְכִנּוּיֵי
דְּאִנְדַּרְנָא וּדְאִשְׁתַּבַּעְנָא וּדְאַחֲרִימְנָא
וּדְאָסַרְנָא עַל נַפְשָׁתָנָא.

All vows, oaths and promises to God with which
we have bound ourselves shall be nullified.

V'AL KULOM

ku - tom....... e-lo-ha......... s'li - - ḥos s'laḥ lo-nu s'- laḥ..... lo-nu s'-

laḥ..... lo-nu m'-ḥal.... lo-nu ka - - - per... lo - nu.

וְעַל כֻּלָם אֱלוֹהַ סְלִיחוֹת
סְלַח לָנוּ, מְחַל לָנוּ, כַּפֶּר־לָנוּ.

O Lord of forgiveness, forgive us for all our sins.

OLENU

Slowly

O - le - nu l'-sha - - - bey-aḥ, la-a - don.... ha - - kol,..... lo-

ses g'-du-lo l'-yo-tzer............ bre-shis, she-lo o --so -- nu k'-go-ye ho-a-ro-
tzos v'-lo so-mo ------- nu, k'-mish-p'-ḥos ho-a-do --mo... she-
lo.... som ḥel-ke --- nu ko-hem v'-go-ro-le-nu k'-ḥol ha-mo-nom.

עָלֵינוּ לְשַׁבֵּחַ לַאֲדוֹן הַכֹּל
לָתֵת גְּדֻלָה לְיוֹצֵר בְּרֵאשִׁית,
שֶׁלֹּא עָשָׂנוּ כְּגוֹיֵי הָאֲרָצוֹת,
וְלֹא שָׂמָנוּ, כְּמִשְׁפְּחוֹת הָאֲדָמָה,
שֶׁלֹּא שָׂם חֶלְקֵנוּ כָּהֶם,
וְגוֹרָלֵנוּ כְּכָל הֲמוֹנָם.

It is meet that we praise the Lord who distinguished
us from other peoples.

94

OPEN THE GATES

In march rhythm

O-pen the gates of right-eous-ness! I will en-ter and praise the Lord.

O-pen the gates of right-eous-ness! I will en-ter and praise the Lord.

This is the day that the Lord hath made, We'll re-joice and be hap-py there-in.

This is the day that the Lord hath made, We'll re-joice and be hap-py there-in.

95

LAMA SUKKAH ZU

WHAT'S OUR SUKKAH FOR?

לָמָה סֻכָּה זוֹ, אַבָּא טוֹב שֶׁלִי? (2)
לֵישֵׁב בַּסֻּכָּה, יַקִירִי, לֵישֵׁב בַּסֻּכָּה, חֲבִיבִי,
לֵישֵׁב בַּסֻּכָּה, יֶלֶד חֵן, יֶלֶד חֵן שֶׁלִי. (2)

לָמָה לֵישֵׁב בָּהּ, אַבָּא טוֹב שֶׁלִי? (2)
אֲבוֹתֵינוּ, יַקִירִי, אֲבוֹתֵינוּ, חֲבִיבִי,
אֲבוֹתֵינוּ אַף גַּם הֵמָּה יָשְׁבוּ בַּסֻּכָּה. (2)

מַה בַּקֻּפְסָה יֵשׁ, אַבָּא טוֹב שֶׁלִי? (2)
אֶתְרוֹג, אֶתְרוֹג, יַקִירִי, אֶתְרוֹג, אֶתְרוֹג, חֲבִיבִי,
אֶתְרוֹג, אֶתְרוֹג, יֶלֶד חֵן, יֶלֶד חֵן שֶׁלִי. (2)

La-ma le-shev ba, a-ba tov she-li? (2)
A-vo-tey-nu, ya-ki-ri, a-vo-tey-nu, ha-vi-vi
A-vo-tey-nu af gam hey-ma yash-vu ba-su-ka. (2)

Ma ba-kuf-sa yesh, a-ba tov she-li? (2)
Et-rog, et-rog, ya-ki-ri, et-rog, et-rog, ha-vi-vi,
Et-rog, et-rog, ye-led hen, ye-led hen she-li. (2)

What's in this little box?
Father, pray do tell;
What does it contain?
Please explain it well.

A yellow *Etrog*, little one,
From Israel, my little son,
For *Sukkot* blessing, dearest one,
Dearest child of mine.

What's this rustling thing?
Father, pray do tell;
A stick to which leaves cling?
Please explain it well.

A *lulav* green, little one,
A branch of palm, little son,
For festive beauty, dearest one,
Dearest child of mine.

SISU V'SIMHU

REJOICE AND BE HAPPY

שִׂישׂוּ וְשִׂמְחוּ בְּשִׂמְחַת חָג,
מַחֲאוּ כַפַּיִם!
נְגְּנוּ שִׁיר בְּקוֹל חָזָק
וּבְמְצִלְתַּיִם.

יָד אֶל יָד כֻּלָּנוּ כְּאֶחָד,
כֹּה בַּסָּך נַעֲבֹרָה,
שֶׁבַח לָאֵל, כִּי לְיִשְׂרָאֵל
הָיְתָה שִׂמְחָה וְאוֹרָה.

YOM TOV LANU

SIMHAT TORAH

99

CHORUS

Ya-ḥad et ha-ḥag na-hog,
On! On! March a-long!

B' lu lav, ha-das, et-roa,
All our voi-ces join in song.

Hoi he-ḥah, nis-mah m'-od
Hear the mel-o-dy live-ly gay;

U-va-ma—gal nir-kod.
This is Sim-hat To-rah day.

All dressed up for this occasion,
There's a sparkle in each glance.
Not a soul that needs persuasion,
To step blithely in a dance.

CHORUS

Apples, banners bobbing gaily,
Carried high by the happy throng.
Torah must be studied daily,
That's the spirit of our song.

CHORUS

יוֹם טוֹב לָנוּ, חַג שָׂמֵחַ,
יְלָדִים, נָגִילָה נָא!
לְסֻכָּתֵנוּ בָּא אוֹרֵחַ:
*אַבְרָהָם אָבִינוּ, בָּרוּךְ הַבָּא.

יַחַד אֶת הַחַג נָחֹג,
בְּלוּלָב, הֲדַס, אֶתְרוֹג;
הוֹי הָאָח, נִשְׂמַח מְאֹד,
וּבַמַּעְגָּל נִרְקֹד.

‎(2) *יִצְחָק אָבִינוּ . . .
‎(3) *יַעֲקֹב רוֹעֵנוּ . . .

Joyously

Cut down the gol-den wheat, Bind it in stur - dy sheaves, oh! Pluck off the jui-cy

grapes, Heap them in bas-kets high. Build a Su -kah co- vered with leaves,

O - pen to the sky, for Now that our har - vest is in,

Slowly

Hal - le - lu - yah. Hal - le - lu - yah, Hal - le - lu - yah we cry!

BROHOS

Blessed art Thou, O Lord, who hast commanded us to shake the Lulav. Blessed art Thou, who hast brought us into this season.

With religious feeling

Bo - ruh a - to A - do - noi E - lo - he -nu me-leh ho-o - lom, a-

sher ki-d'- sho - nu b'- mitz - vo - sov v'-tzi - vo-nu al n'ti-las lu-

lov. Bo - ruh a - to A - do - noi e - lo - he -nu me-leh ho-o - lom, she-

he- he-yo - nu v'-ki-y'- mo- nu v'- hi- gi - o - nu la - 3'- man ha - 3e.

בָּרוּךְ אַתָּה יְיָ אֱלֹהֵינוּ מֶלֶךְ הָעוֹלָם,
אֲשֶׁר קִדְּשָׁנוּ בְּמִצְוֹתָיו וְצִוָּנוּ עַל
נְטִילַת לוּלָב:

בָּרוּךְ אַתָּה יְיָ אֱלֹהֵינוּ מֶלֶךְ הָעוֹלָם,
שֶׁהֶחֱיָנוּ וְקִיְּמָנוּ וְהִגִּיעָנוּ לַזְּמַן הַזֶּה:

ONO ADONOI

Save us, answer us, O Lord, O Mighty Redeemer,
when we call unto Thee.

אָנָּא יְיָ הוֹשִׁיעָה נָא:

אָנָּא יְיָ הַצְלִיחָה נָא:

אָנָּא יְיָ עֲנֵנוּ בְיוֹם קָרְאֵנוּ:

E-lo-hey ho-ru-ḥos ho-shi-o no:

Bo-ḥen l'vo-vos hatz-li-ḥo no:

Go-el ḥo-zok a-ne-nu v'yom kor-e-nu:

אֱלֹהֵי הָרוּחוֹת הוֹשִׁיעָה נָא:

בּוֹחֵן לְבָבוֹת הַצְלִיחָה נָא:

גּוֹאֵל חָזָק עֲנֵנוּ בְיוֹם קָרְאֵנוּ:

103

KAHA N'RAKEDA

tra-la-la-la-la-la-la-la tra-la-la-la tra-la-la-la-la-la-la-la tra-la-la-la

tra-la-la-la-la-la-la-la tra-la-la-la tra-la-la-la-la-la-la-la la.

(4) נְרַקֵּדָה, כָּכָה כָּכָה כָּכָה
נְרַקֵּדָה. 2{

שְׂאוּ כַּפַּיִם לַשָּׁמַיִם, (2) לַשָּׁמַיִם. 2{

הוֹי, הִתְעוֹרְרוּ, הִתְעוֹרְרוּ,
טְרַלָה. . . .

So shall we dance, hands raised to the sky. Up, up!
Tra la la!

KI V'SIMḤA TETZE'U

FOR IN GLADNESS

Rhythmically

Ki v'sim-ḥa te-tze--u   u—v'-sa-son.... tu-
For in..... glad-ness, you'll go.... forth,   tho* the ...... jour-ney,

va—lun,   He- ha— rim v'-ha-g'va-ot   yif-tz'— ḥu ri-
may be long.   The hills and the val—leys   will re-sound   with joy-ous, joy-ous

na.   U— sh'av-tem ma-yim b'-sa-son........   mi-ma-ay-ney... ha-
song.   And   you'll draw wa-ter   in great joy........   from the..... foun—tains

y'—shu— a;.....   Tza-ha-li, tza-ha— li va-ro-ni, yo— she-vet Tzi-yon,.... yo-
of sal—va-tion!   Oh re-joice, re — joice and sing you who dwell in........ Zi --on,

(*Round   Group 2 begins when Group I reaches
the*)

106

she - vet Tzi - yon.   Hal - le - lu — yah,   hal - le - lu — yah.
bles- sed   na - tion.

כִּי בְשִׂמְחָה תֵצֵאוּ, וּבְשָׁלוֹם תּוּבָלוּן,
*הֶהָרִים וְהַגְּבָעוֹת יִפְצְחוּ רִנָה.
וּשְׁאַבְתֶּם מַיִם בְּשָׂשׂוֹן מִמַּעַיְנֵי
הַיְשׁוּעָה:
צַהֲלִי, צַהֲלִי וָרֹנִי, יוֹשֶׁבֶת צִיוֹן,
יוֹשֶׁבֶת צִיוֹן, הַלְלוּיָהּ, הַלְלוּיָהּ.

MY CANDLES

Hanukah

Slowly

1. In the win-dow where you can send your glow From
2. In the win-dow where you can send your glow From

my Me-no-rah on new-ly fal-len snow, I will set you,*one
my Me-no-rah on new-ly fal-len snow, I will set you, two

lit-tle can-dle, On this the *first....... night of Ha-nu-kah.
lit-tle can-dles, On this the se-cond night of Ha-nu-kah.

*On each of the nights of Hanukah, sing the correct number.

Lively

I have a lit-tle drey-dl, I made it out of clay; And when it's dry and rea-dy Then drey-dl I shall play. O drey-dl, drey-dl, drey-dl, I made it out of clay; O drey-dl, drey-dl, drey-dl, Now drey-dl I shall play.

It has a lovely body,
    With leg so short and thin;
And when it is all tired,
    It drops and then I win.
    O *dreydl, dreydl, dreydl,*
    With leg so short and thin;
    O *dreydl, dreydl, dreydl,*
    It drops and then I win.

My *dreydl* is always playful,
    It loves to dance and spin.
A happy game of *dreydl,*
    Come play, now let's begin.
    O *dreydl, dreydl, dreydl,*
    It loves to dance and spin.
    O *dreydl, dreydl, dreydl,*
    Come play, now let's begin.

S'VIVON

S'-vi-von, sov, sov, sov, Ha-nu-kah.......... hu hag tov!

Ha-nu-kah hu hag tov!..... S'-vi-von,...... sov, sov, sov.

Hag sim-ha...... hu la-am,...... Nes ga-dol ha-ya......... sham!

Nes ga-dol ha-ya sham!...... Hag sim-ha..... hu la-am.

Little dreydl, *spin, spin, spin.* Ḥanukah is a day of joy. Great was the miracle that happened there. *Spin, little* dreydl, *spin, spin, spin.*

סְבִיבוֹן, סֹב, סֹב, סֹב,
חֲנֻכָּה הוּא חַג טוֹב!
חֲנֻכָּה הוּא חַג טוֹב!
סְבִיבוֹן, סֹב, סֹב, סֹב.

חַג שִׂמְחָה הוּא לָעָם,
נֵס גָּדוֹל הָיָה שָׁם!
נֵס גָּדוֹל הָיָה שָׁם!
חַג שִׂמְחָה הוּא לָעָם.

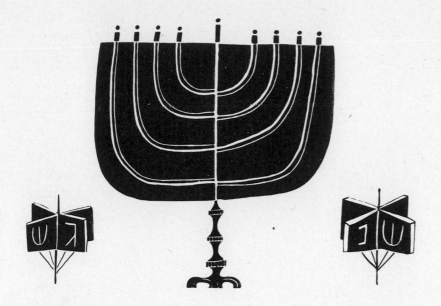

HANUKAH

With Spirit

Ha-nu-kah, ha-nu-kah, hag ya-fe kol kah..... Or ha-viv mi-sa-viv, gil l'-ye-led rah......... Ha-nu-kah, ha-nu-kah,

s'—vi-von sov, sov,........ Sov, sov, sov, sov, sov, sov, Ma na-im va—tov.

Ḥanukah is a merry holiday. Tops spin 'round,
candles burn. Oh, let us sing and dance.

Ha-nu-kah, Ha-nu-kah, en ḥa-lon b'li esh.
L'vi-vot, suf-ga-ni-yot b'ḥol ba-yit yesh.
Ha-nu-kah, Ha-nu-kah, ḥag ḥa-viv m'od.
Shi-ru na, zam-ru na.
U-tz'u lir-kod.

חֲנֻכָּה, חֲנֻכָּה, חַג יָפֶה כָּל כַּךְ.
אוֹר חָבִיב מִסָּבִיב, גִּיל לְיֶלֶד רַךְ.
חֲנֻכָּה, חֲנֻכָּה, סְבִיבוֹן, סֹב, סֹב,
סֹב, סֹב, סֹב, סֹב, סֹב, סֹב,
מַה נָּעִים וָטוֹב.

חֲנֻכָּה, חֲנֻכָּה, אֵין חַלוֹן בְּלִי אֵשׁ.
לְבִיבוֹת, סֻפְגָּנִיּוֹת בְּכָל בַּיִת יֵשׁ.
חֲנֻכָּה, חֲנֻכָּה, חַג חָבִיב מְאֹד.
שִׁירוּ נָא, זַמְּרוּ נָא,
וּצְאוּ לִרְקוֹד.

ḤANUKAH PANCAKES

la la la la la la,　la la　la　la,　la　la　la　la,　La la la la la la　la......

Ke-maḥ, ke-maḥ min ha-sak,

She-men, she-men min ha-kad.

Ha-va n'la-bev,

L'vi-vot la-ḥag.

La, la, la.

Od no-sif be-tsa mi-sal,

Od su-kar dak, v'ha-sal.

Bo-u la-shul-ḥan,

L'vi-vot no-ḥal.

La, la, la.

Mix the flour so snowy white,

With the oil so golden bright,

That's how mother makes

Ḥanukah pancakes!

La, la, la . . . .

Add an egg; the batter's done,

And some sugar; O what fun.

Come now take your seats,

Steaming pancakes eat.

La, la, la . . . .

קֶמַח, קֶמַח מִן הַשַּׂק,
שֶׁמֶן, שֶׁמֶן מִן הַכַּד.
חֲנֻכָּה הַיּוֹם,
חַג נָעִים נֶחְמָד!
לַ, לַ, לַ.

קֶמַח, קֶמַח מִן הַשַּׂק,
שֶׁמֶן, שֶׁמֶן מִן הַכַּד.
הָבָה נְלַבֵּב,
לְבִיבוֹת לַחַג.
לַ, לַ, לַ.

עוֹד נוֹסִיף בֵּיצָה מִסַּל,
עוֹד סוּכָּר דַּק, וְחַסַּל.
בּוֹאוּ לַשֻּׁלְחָן,
לְבִיבוֹת נֹאכַל.
לַ, לַ, לַ.

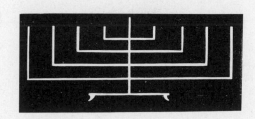

SPIN, MY TOP

In a jolly manner

Sov, sov, sov, sov, sov s'-vi-von, Mi-ru-sha-la-yim l-Giv-on. Mi-Giv-on, sov ad Bet El, U-mi-sham l' Yiz-r'--el. Sham k' hal ha-lu-tzim B'-ma-hol ku-lam yotz-im. Sov, sov, s'-vi-von, Ru-tza, u-tza l'-Giv-on.

Spin, my top, a—round and a-round O, spin past bush and pit and mound, Past the vine—yard, brook and rill, Past the val-ley and the hill, On to Kish-on, my dear When you meet a pi-o—neer, Greet him, bring him cheer; "Mi-ra-cles have hap-pened here!"

Sov, sov, sov, sov, sov s'vi-von,

Mi-ru-sha-la-yim l'Gi-von.

Ba-ma-gal hi-ka-nes,

V'la-kol b'kol haḥ-rez:

Hi-ne kam, ha-ya ha-nes,

Kol ha-a-retz k'far-des,

Mi-B'er She-va v'ad Dan,

Kol ha-a-retz haf-ḥa gan.

Unto Modin swiftly fly,

And your tidings shout and cry:

"Maccabeans, rest ye in peace,

Lo, your valiant heirs increase.

Now in place of waging war

They plant vineyards by the score,

Toiling hard, hauling loads,

Building houses, paving roads."

סֹב, סֹב, סֹב, סֹב, סֹב סְבִיבוֹן,
מִירוּשָׁלַיִם לְגִבְעוֹן.
בְּמַעְגַּל הַכְּנֵס,
וְלַכֹּל בְּקוֹל הַכְרֵז:
הִנֵּה קָם, הָיָה הַנֵּס,
כָּל הָאָרֶץ – כְּפַרְדֵּס,
מִבְּאֵר שֶׁבַע וְעַד דָּן,
כָּל הָאָרֶץ הָפְכָה גַן.

סֹב, סֹב, סֹב, סֹב, סֹב סְבִיבוֹן,
מִירוּשָׁלַיִם לְגִבְעוֹן.
מִגִּבְעוֹן סֹב עַד בֵּית אֵל,
וּמִשָּׁם לְיִזְרְעֶאל.
שָׁם קְהַל חֲלוּצִים
בְּמָחוֹל כֻּלָּם יוֹצְאִים.
סֹב, סֹב, סְבִיבוֹן,
רוּצָה, אוּצָה לְגִבְעוֹן.

Y'HUDA HAMAKABI

Ka - ma-ke-vet, Ka - pa - tish..... Ko ḥa-zak Ha - ya ha - ish.....

Uv' - li - bo..... Rak esh, esh: Ha - kot o - y'vim, Ga - resh, ga-resh! Nil-

-ham har-bey, O — y'vim gey-rash, Ti — her, hi-desh Bet ha-mik-dash Hid-

-lik u rim... L' — dor va-dor... Ba — or, hid-lik, ... Gam la-nu or.........

כַּמַּקֶּבֶת,
כַּפַּטִּישׁ —
כֹּה חָזָק
הָיָה הָאִישׁ.

וּבְלִבּוֹ
רַק אֵשׁ, אֵשׁ:
הַכּוֹת אוֹיְבִים,
גָּרֵשׁ, גָּרֵשׁ!

נִלְחַם הַרְבֵּה,
אוֹיְבִים גֵּרֵשׁ,
טִהֵר, חִדֵּשׁ
בֵּית־הַמִּקְדָּשׁ.

הִדְלִיק אוּרִים
לְדוֹר וָדוֹר.
בָּאוֹר הִדְלִיק
גַּם לָנוּ אוֹר ...

He was strong as a hammer, and in his heart a flame: strike, drive the enemy from the land. The lights he kindled in the Temple continue to shine through the ages.

117

MI Y'MALEL

*WHO CAN RETELL

Round — group II begins song when group I has reached.

**) Second version.

118

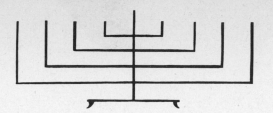

de...... U — v'ya-mey — nu kol am yis — ra —
band.................... But now all Is — rael must as one a —

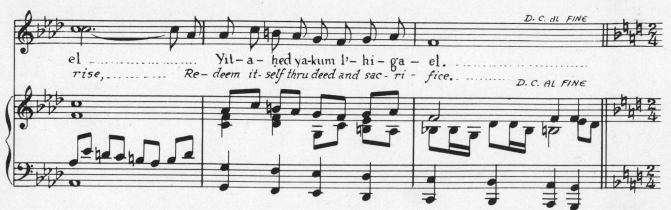

el .... Yit — a — ḥed ya-kum l'— hi — ga — el.
rise,.............. Re — deem it- self thru deed and sac — ri — fice.

D. C. AL FINE

מִי יְמַלֵּל גְּבוּרוֹת יִשְׂרָאֵל?
*אוֹתָן מִי יִמְנֶה?
הֵן בְּכָל דּוֹר יָקוּם הַגִּבּוֹר,
גּוֹאֵל הָעָם.

מִי יְמַלֵּל גְּבוּרוֹת יְיָ?** *

שְׁמַע! בַּיָּמִים הָהֵם בַּזְּמַן הַזֶּה
מַכַּבִּי מוֹשִׁיעַ וּפוֹדֶה.
וּבְיָמֵינוּ כָּל עַם יִשְׂרָאֵל
יִתְאַחֵד יָקוּם לְהִגָּאֵל!

119

Y'MEY HAHANUKAH

HANUKAH, O HANUKAH

Moderato

Y' - mey ha-ha-nu - kah,.... ha-nu - kat mik-da - she-nu, B' - gil........ uv-sim-
O Ha-nu-ka, O Ha-nu-ka, a fes-ti-val of joy,...... A ho-li-day, a

hah.... m'mal-im...... et li - bey-nu; Lai - la va - yom s'vi-vo-
jol-ly day, for every girl and boy,........ Spin the whir-ling "tren-dles"

ne-nu yi - sov, Suf - ga - ni - yot no - hal bam la - rov! rov! Ha-
all week long, Eat the siz-zling "lat-kes," sing the hap-py songs! songs! Now

i - ru had - li - ku Ne - rot Ha-nu-kah ra - bim!........
light then to - night then, the flicke-ring...... can-dels in a row,........

120

Nitz-ḥon ha-Ma-ka-bim n'sa-per, n'za-me-ra,
A-ley ha-so-n'im az ya-dam ki ga-ve-ra;
Y'ru-sha-la-yim sha-va lit-ḥi-ya;
Am Yis-ra-el a-sa tu-shi-ya.

CHORUS

Brave Judah Maccabee put the enemy to rout,
And from the holy Temple he drove the
    tyrants out,
'Twas then in old Jerusalem that freedom was
    attained,
And oil of gladness filled the lamp, the Torah
    lamp regained.

Come sing then, and bring then

All honor to the brave Maccabees.

Let kinsmen and brethren sing praises
  together

And thank God for the light which is His.

יְמֵי הַחֲנֻכָּה, חֲנֻכַּת מִקְדָּשֵׁנוּ,
בְּגִיל וּבְשִׂמְחָה מְמַלְּאִים אֶת לִבֵּנוּ;
לַיְלָה וָיוֹם סְבִיבוֹנֵנוּ יִסֹּב,
סֻפְגָּנִיּוֹת נֹאכַל בָּם לָרֹב.

מקהלה:
הָאִירוּ, הַדְלִיקוּ
נֵרוֹת חֲנֻכָּה רַבִּים!
עַל הַנִּסִּים וְעַל הַנִּפְלָאוֹת
אֲשֶׁר חוֹלְלוּ מַכַּבִּים.

נִצְחוֹן הַמַּכַּבִּים נְסַפֵּר, נְזַמֵּרָה,
עֲלֵי הַשּׂוֹנְאִים אָז יָדָם כִּי גָבְרָה;
יְרוּשָׁלַיִם שָׁבָה לִתְחִיָּה;
עַם יִשְׂרָאֵל עָשָׂה תּוּשִׁיָּה.

(מקהלה)

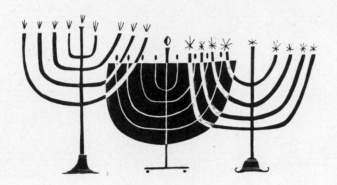

HEAR THE VOICE

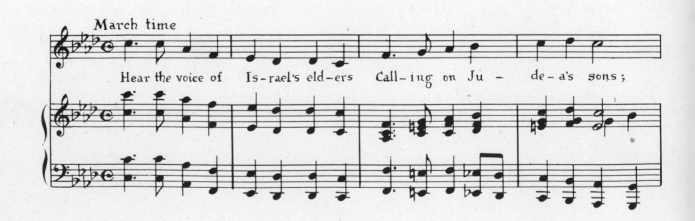

Hear the voice of Is-rael's eld-ers Call-ing on Ju — de-a's sons;

"Who will be the fu-ture lead-ers When the eld-er men are gone?

Who will do what we have start-ed, Bring the Jew to an-cient sta-tion

Who will urge the wea-ry heart-ed Fight for right and live a na-tion?"

Hear the brave and youthful heroes
   Coming onward with the call,
"When we're one, oppressors fear us,
   Courage, courage, brothers all.
Israel's patriots and sages
   Taught us how to live like men
Israel's youth, with hearts courageous,
   Live for God and faith again."

"Every Jew is each man's brother,
   Fighting on for God and right;
Fearless, cheering one another,
   Aiding all with main and might.
Hopeful-hearted, helpful-handed,
   Join in union every Jew.
God will help us when we're banded
   Build the nation up anew."

MATTATHIAS

With martial spirit

1. He

struck the trai-tor to the earth; He raised his sword that all might see; His
near and far all Is - rael came; They ral - lied to his bat-tle cry; They

words rang like a trum-pet blast:...... "All who are faith-ful fol - low me!"
prayed un-to the God of Peace,......

2. From

And for their law went forth to die. To die........ and yet to - day they live; Far

down the cen-turies' flow-ing sea.......... That bea-con sword! Hear that strong cry:......... "All who are

1.
faith-ful, fol-low me!"........ To

2.
faith — ful............ fol — low me!".......

OH, COME, MY DREYDL

Lightly

Oh, come, my drey-dl, my drey-dl of tin, Dance a — bout mer— ri—ly, dance and spin! Dance o—ver prai-rie Dance, spin and reel, Light and ai — ry, Like a spin-ning wheel. Make way for my drey-dl, his whirl and sweep, One step is a league, and a mile.... his... leap He's off with a bound Like a

stal-lion....... bold. Hur— rah! He has found A moun-tain of gold!

D. C. AL FINE

D. C. AL FINE

Oh, rush to the mountain! Make way, make
  way!
Seize the treasure without delay!
     Go win it, O
     My *dreydl* of tin,
     Before my foe
     Can say, "I win!"

Then tipsy, it staggered, back, until
Down it went — my heart stood still . . .
     Gimel! Oh, joy!
     Come all and see
     How my spinning toy
     Has won for me.

Oh, great is the miracle that happened
  there,
There is no other that can compare!
     The game we played
Is at an end.
My pockets bulge.
Goodbye, my friend.

B'ROḤOS SHEL ḤANUKAH

*) *The 3rd blessing is said only on the first night. Repeat the first 6 meas. of the 1st blessing and continue with the following.*

ki - mo - nu...... v'- hi-gi-o - nu laz'- man ha — ze. O ----- men.

Blessed art Thou, O Lord, who hast commanded us to kindle the Ḥanukah lights. Blessed art Thou, who hast wrought miracles for our fathers in those days. Blessed art Thou who hast brought us unto this season.

בָּרוּךְ אַתָּה יְיָ אֱלֹהֵינוּ מֶלֶךְ הָעוֹלָם
אֲשֶׁר קִדְּשָׁנוּ בְּמִצְוֹתָיו וְצִוָּנוּ
לְהַדְלִיק נֵר שֶׁל חֲנֻכָּה.

בָּרוּךְ אַתָּה יְיָ אֱלֹהֵינוּ מֶלֶךְ הָעוֹלָם
שֶׁעָשָׂה נִסִּים לַאֲבוֹתֵינוּ בַּיָּמִים הָהֵם
בַּזְּמַן הַזֶּה.

בָּרוּךְ אַתָּה יְיָ אֱלֹהֵינוּ מֶלֶךְ הָעוֹלָם
שֶׁהֶחֱיָנוּ וְקִיְּמָנוּ וְהִגִּיעָנוּ לַזְּמַן הַזֶּה.

MO'OZ TZUR

ROCK OF AGES

Mo-oz tzur y'- shu-o-si l'ho no-e l'sha-bey — ah, Ti-kon bes t'-
Rock of A-ges, let our song Praise Thy sav-ing pow — er; Thou, a-midst the

fi-lo-si v'shom to-do n'za — bey — ah. L'es to-hin mat-bey-ah mi-tzor-
rag-ing foes, Wast our shelt-'ring tow — er. Fu-rious, they as — sailed us, But Thine arm a-

ha-m'na-be-ah, Oz eg-mor b'-shir miz-mor, ha-nu-kas ha-miz-bey-ah.
vail — ed us, And Thy word....... Broke their sword... When our own strength failed us.

Y'vo-nim nik-b'tzu o-lai, a-zai bi-mey ḥash-ma-nim,

U-for-tzu ḥo-mos mig-do-lai v'tim-u kol hash-mo-nim.

U-mi-no-sar kan-ka-nim na-a-se nes l'sho-sha-nim,

B'ney vi-no y'mey sh'mo-no kov-u shir u-r'no-nim.

מָעוֹז צוּר יְשׁוּעָתִי לְךָ נָאָה לְשַׁבֵּחַ,
תִּכּוֹן בֵּית תְּפִלָּתִי וְשָׁם תּוֹדָה נְזַבֵּחַ.
לְעֵת תָּכִין מַטְבֵּחַ מִצָּר הַמְנַבֵּחַ,
אָז אֶגְמֹר בְּשִׁיר מִזְמוֹר,
חֲנֻכַּת הַמִּזְבֵּחַ.

יְוָנִים נִקְבְּצוּ עָלַי אֲזַי בִּימֵי חַשְׁמַנִּים,
וּפָרְצוּ חוֹמוֹת מִגְדָּלַי וְטִמְּאוּ כָּל הַשְּׁמָנִים.
וּמִנּוֹתַר קַנְקַנִּים נַעֲשָׂה נֵס לַשּׁוֹשַׁנִּים,
בְּנֵי בִינָה יְמֵי שְׁמוֹנָה קָבְעוּ שִׁיר וּרְנָנִים.

Children of the Martyr-race,
Whether free or fettered,
Wake the echoes of the songs
Where ye may be scattered.
Yours the message cheering
That the time is nearing
Which will see
All men free,
Tyrants disappearing.

AL HANISIM

Moderato

CHORUS

Al ha-ni-sim v'al ha-pur-kon v'—al ha-g'vu-ros v'al ha-t'shu-os

she—o-si-so la—avo-sey—nu la—avo-se-nu ba—yo—mim ho-hem

FINE

ba—z'—man ha—ze: Bi—mey Ma—tis—yo—hu Ma-tis-

-yo-hu ben Yo—ho-non ko—hen go—dol hash-mo-no-i u—

vo - nov k' she - om — — do...... mal - hus yo - von...... al

am — ho Yis - ro — el al am - ho Yis - ro — el l' - hash - ki - hom..... to -

ro - se — ho ul - ha - vi — rom me - hu - key r' - tzo - ne - ho   Al hanisim   V' - a -
                                                                    𝄋 CHORUS

to b' - ra - ha — me - ho........ b' — ra - ha - me - ho ho - ra -
to lo — hem b'eys tzo -

132

-bim .... o-ma-d'- ro-som b'- rah-me- ho ho-ra — bim. At hanisim
CHORUS

מקהלה:

עַל הַנִּסִּים וְעַל הַפֻּרְקָן וְעַל
הַגְּבוּרוֹת וְעַל הַתְּשׁוּעוֹת שֶׁעָשִׂיתָ
לַאֲבוֹתֵינוּ בַּיָּמִים הָהֵם בַּזְּמַן הַזֶּה:

בִּימֵי מַתִּתְיָהוּ בֶּן־יוֹחָנָן כֹּהֵן גָּדוֹל
חַשְׁמוֹנַאי וּבָנָיו כְּשֶׁעָמְדָה מַלְכוּת יָוָן
עַל עַמְּךָ יִשְׂרָאֵל לְהַשְׁכִּיחָם תּוֹרָתֶךָ
וּלְהַעֲבִירָם מֵחֻקֵּי רְצוֹנֶךָ:

עַל הַנִּסִּים וְעַל הַפֻּרְקָן . . .

וְאַתָּה בְּרַחֲמֶיךָ הָרַבִּים עָמַדְתָּ לָהֶם
בְּעֵת צָרָתָם.

עַל הַנִּסִּים וְעַל הַפֻּרְקָן . . .

*We thank Thee for the miracle Thou didst accom-
plish for our fathers in those days, at this season.
When the Greeks sought to destroy Thy people and
Thy Torah, Thou, in Thy mercy, didst save them
from destruction.*

HANEROS HALOLU

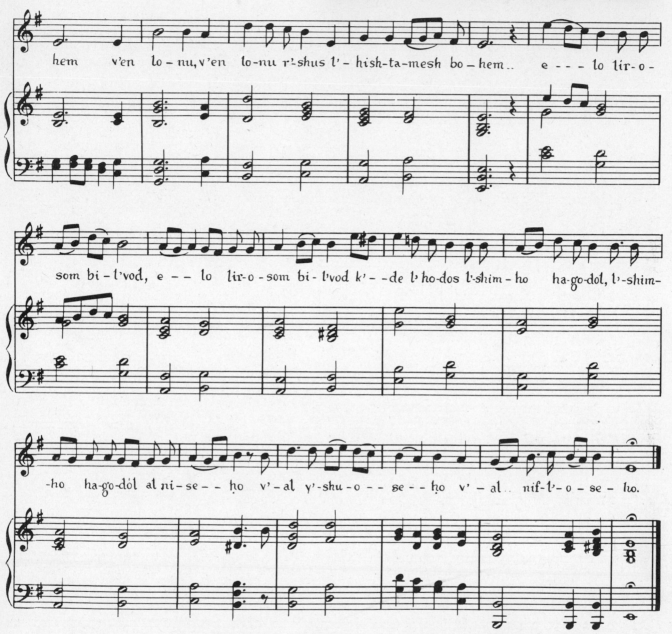

hem v'en lo-nu, v'en lo-nu r'shus l'-hish-ta-mesh bo-hem.. e - - lo lir-o-

som bi-l'vod, e - - lo lir-o-som bi-l'vod k'-de l'ho-dos l'shim-ho ha-go-dol, l'shim-

-ho ha-go-dol al ni-se - - ho v'-al y'-shu-o - - se - - ho v'-al nif-l'-o-se - - ho.

הַנֵּרוֹת הַלָּלוּ קֹדֶשׁ הֵם וְאֵין
לָנוּ רְשׁוּת לְהִשְׁתַּמֵּשׁ בָּהֶם אֶלָּא
לִרְאוֹתָם בִּלְבָד כְּדֵי לְהוֹדוֹת
לִשְׁמְךָ הַגָּדוֹל עֲלִנִסֶּיךָ וְעַל-
יְשׁוּעָתְךָ וְעַל נִפְלְאוֹתֶיךָ.

הַנֵּרוֹת הַלָּלוּ אֲנַחְנוּ מַדְלִיקִין
עַל הַנִּסִּים וְעַל הַתְּשׁוּעוֹת וְעַל
הַנִּפְלָאוֹת שֶׁעָשִׂיתָ לַאֲבוֹתֵינוּ בַּיָּמִים
הָהֵם בַּזְּמַן הַזֶּה עַל יְדֵי כֹּהֲנֶיךָ
הַקְּדוֹשִׁים. וְכָל שְׁמוֹנַת יְמֵי חֲנֻכָּה

136

through Thy holy priests. These Ḥanukah lights
are holy, and through them we sanctify Thy name.

hol sh'mo-nas y'mey ha — nu — — koh ha-ne — ros ha — lo-lu ko-desh hem......... v'eyn

lo-nu r'-shus l'-hish-ta — mesh bo — hem e — lo lir-o-som bil' — vod. K'—

a tempo

dey...... l'-ho — dos..... l'-shim — ḥo......... ha-go — dol....... al ni-

se — ho v'al y' — shu-o — se-ho v' — al nif-l'-o — se — ḥo......

B'RAHA L'TU BISH'VAT

Liltingly

Ki ta-vo-u el........ ha-a-retz Un'-ta-tem kol

etz..... t'hi-la..... V'-na-tan ha-etz pir-yo...... V'-ha-

-a-retz y'-vu-la.... Et lin-to-a i-la-not,.... et lin-

to — a i — la — not......... et lin—to—a i—la—not.

When you come to the land and plant trees, and trees and soil give forth their abundance, then shall you be like a tree planted by the waters.

כִּי תָבֹאוּ אֶל הָאָרֶץ
וּנְטַעְתֶּם כָּל עֵץ תְּחִלָּה.
וְנָתַן הָעֵץ פִּרְיוֹ
וְהָאָרֶץ יְבוּלָהּ.
עֵת לִנְטֹעַ אִילָנוֹת (3).

Vi-shav-tem ish ta-ḥat gaf-no
V'ta-ḥat t'e-na-to,
Va-ha-yi-tem k'etz sha-tul
Al pal-gey ma-yim.
　　Et lin-to-a i-la-not (3).

וִישַׁבְתֶּם אִישׁ תַּחַת גַּפְנוֹ
וְתַחַת תְּאֵנָתוֹ,
וִהְיִיתֶם כְּעֵץ שָׁתוּל
עַל פַּלְגֵי מַיִם.
עֵת לִנְטֹעַ אִילָנוֹת (3).

U-v'ni-tem ḥor-vot o-lam
Sho-m'mot t'ko-m'mu.
Va-ḥa-yi-tem al ad-mat-ḥem
La-ve-taḥ u-l'o-lam.
　　Et lin-to-a i-la-not (3).

וּבְנִיתֶם חָרְבוֹת עוֹלָם
שׁוֹמְמוֹת תְּקוֹמְמוּ.
וַחֲיִיתֶם עַל אַדְמַתְכֶם
לָבֶטַח וּלְעוֹלָם.
עֵת לִנְטֹעַ אִילָנוֹת (3).

HASHKEDIYA

TU BISHVAT IS HERE

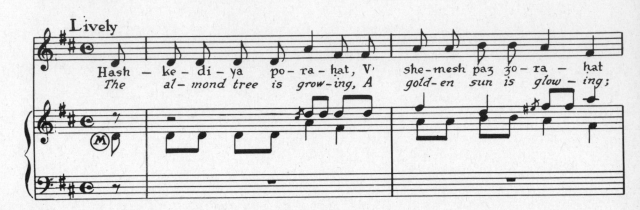

Ha-a-retz m'sha-va-at:

Hi-gi-a et la-ta-at.

Kol e-ḥad yi-kaḥ lo etz,

Ba-i-tim ne-tze ḥo-tzetz:

Tu bi-Sh'vat . . . .

Let's make the land a garden,

With water from the Jordan;

And our land will flow once more

With milk and honey, as of yore.

CHORUS

140

Ni-ta kol har va-ge-va
Mi-Dan v'ad B'er She-va.
V'ar-tzę-nu shuv ni-rash
E-retz za-yit, ḥa-lav u-d'vash.
Tu bi-Sh'vat . . . .

נְטַע כָּל הַר וָגֶבַע | הָאָרֶץ מְשַׁוַּעַת: | הַשְּׁקֵדִיָּה פּוֹרַחַת,
מִדָּן וְעַד בְּאֵר שָׁבַע. | הִגִּיעָה עֵת לָטַעַת. | וְשֶׁמֶשׁ פָּז זוֹרַחַת.
וְאַרְצֵנוּ שׁוּב נִירַשׁ | כָּל אֶחָד יִקַּח לוֹ עֵץ, | צִפֳּרִים מֵראשׁ כָּל גַּג
אֶרֶץ זַיִת, חָלָב וּדְבַשׁ. | בְּאֵתִים נֵצֵא חוֹצֵץ: | מְבַשְּׂרוֹת אֶת בֹּא הֶחָג:
ט"ו בִּשְׁבָט . . . | ט"ו בִּשְׁבָט . . . | ט"ו בִּשְׁבָט הִגִּיעַ—
חַג הָאִילָנוֹת.

KAH HOLḤIM HASHOTLIM

HERE COME PLANTERS

March

Kaḥ hol-ḥim ha-shot-lim, Ron ba-lev v'-et ba-yad, Min ha-ir u-min ha-k'far,
Here come planters spade in hand, See them swinging brave-ly by, Lit-tle trees they bear on high.

Min ha-ir u-min ha-k'far. B'- Tu, tu tu tu, b'- Tu Bish-vat. B'- Tu Bish-vat.
On Ha-mi-sha A-sar Bish-vat, On Tu, tu tu tu, on Tu Bish-vat. On Tu Bish-vat.

La-ma ba-tem ha-shot-lim?
Naḥ ba-kar-ka u-va-tzor
V'gu-mot sa-viv naḥ-por
Be-ha-rim u-va-mi-shor.

CHORUS

Ma y'hey po, ha-shot-lim?
Sha-til ya-vo b'ḥol gu-ma,
Ya-ar ad yif-ros tzi-lo
Al ar-tze-nu a-gu-ma.

CHORUS

What has brought you planters here?
We strike the rocky mountain side,
Drain the marshes far and wide.

CHORUS

What will all your labors bring?
Trees will clothe the land so bare,
Giving shade and beauty rare.

CHORUS

מַה יְהֵא פֹה, הַשּׁוֹתְלִים?
שָׁתִיל יָבוֹא בְּכָל גּוּמָה,
יַעַר עַד יִפְרֹשׁ צִלּוֹ
עַל אַרְצֵנוּ עֲגוּמָה.
מקהלה: בְּט"ו בִּשְׁבָט.

לָמָה בָּאתֶם הַשּׁוֹתְלִים?
נַךְ בַּקַּרְקַע וּבַצֹּר
וְגוּמוֹת סָבִיב נַחְפֹּר
בֶּהָרִים וּבַמִּישׁוֹר.
מקהלה: בְּט"ו בִּשְׁבָט.

כָּךְ הוֹלְכִים הַשּׁוֹתְלִים
רוֹן בַּלֵּב וְאֵת בַּיָּד,
מִן הָעִיר וּמִן הַכְּפָר,
מִן הָעִיר וּמִן הַכְּפָר.
מקהלה: בְּט"ו בִּשְׁבָט.

ATZEY ZETIM OMDIM

עֲצֵי זֵיתִים עוֹמְדִים.
לַ, לַ, לַ, לַ, לַ, לַ, לַ,
עֲצֵי זֵיתִים עוֹמְדִים.

Olive trees are standing. Olive trees are standing.

L'SHANA TOVA SHKEDIYA

*For third stanza substitute *IIa-ru-va*

Hen, hen, hen y'-la — dim.........., Hey la-ḥem {sh'- ke-dim.
{y'- ka — rim........., {t'- ma-rim.

*For second stanza substitute *Te-ma-ra*

*For third stanza substitute *Ḥa-ru-va*

Happy New Year, almond tree, may the Lord give you sun and dew, soft wind and gentle rain.

Thank you, children. Here are almonds from my boughs.

לְשָׁנָה טוֹבָה, שְׁקֵדִיָּה,
וְיִתֵּן לָךְ אֱלֹהִים
שֶׁמֶשׁ, אוֹר, שֶׁפַע טַל.
גֶּשֶׁם טוֹב, רוּחַ קַל.
חֵן, חֵן, חֵן, יְלָדִים,
הֵא לָכֶם שְׁקֵדִים.

EL HASADE

El ha-sa-de!...... El ha-sa-de! Zu-
B'gil va — shir!...... B'gil va — shir! Zu-

got,......... zu-got......... ne-tze hu-la — nu! V'hol e-had ma-
got,......... zu-got......., ya-mi-na s'mo-la!......... Sham ba-sa-dot, y'la-

145

der ba-yad—Kol ye-led kat ga — nan — hu!.... Ne-tze-a ne-tze-a, ne-tze-a ne-tze-a,
dim, y'la-dot, E — tsim ra-kim nish-to — la!.... Nish-to — la, nish-to — la, b'-

el ha-sa-de ne — tze — a!..........
gil va — shir nish — to — la...........

poco rit.

*Two by two we swing along; off to the meadow
together we go. Each child is a planter, each with
a hoe; tender saplings we shall plant. Each sapling
shall blossom, each child shall grow.*

El ha-sa-de! El ha-sa-de!
Zu-got zu-got nitz-ad ku-la-nu!
Kol etz yitz-maḥ, kol etz yif-raḥ —
Nitz-maḥ, nif-raḥ, gam a-nu!
Ka-di-ma, ka-di-ma, el ha-sa-de,
   ka-di-ma! (2)

אֶל הַשָּׂדֶה! אֶל הַשָּׂדֶה!
זוּגוֹת, זוּגוֹת, נֵצֵא כֻּלָּנוּ!
וְכָל אֶחָד מַעְדֵּר בַּיָּד—
כָּל יֶלֶד קָט גַּנָּן הוּא!
נֵצֵאָה, נֵצֵאָה, אֶל הַשָּׂדֶה נֵצֵאָה! (2)

בְּגִיל וָשִׁיר! בְּגִיל וָשִׁיר!
זוּגוֹת, זוּגוֹת, יָמִינָה שְׂמֹאלָה!
שָׁם בַּשָּׂדוֹת, יְלָדִים, יְלָדוֹת,
עֵצִים רַכִּים נִשְׁתֹּלָה!
נִשְׁתֹּלָה, נִשְׁתֹּלָה, בְּגִיל וָשִׁיר
נִשְׁתֹּלָה! (2)

אֶל הַשָּׂדֶה! אֶל הַשָּׂדֶה!
זוּגוֹת, זוּגוֹת, נִצְעַד כֻּלָּנוּ!
כָּל עֵץ יִצְמַח, כָּל עֵץ יִפְרַח—
נִצְמַח, נִפְרַח, גַּם אָנוּ!
קָדִימָה, קָדִימָה, אֶל הַשָּׂדֶה,
קָדִימָה! (2)

WHEN YOU COME HOME

כִּי תָבֹאוּ אֶל הָאָרֶץ
וּנְטַעְתֶּם כָּל עֵץ.
לִבְנוֹת וְלִנְטֹעַ, לַחֲרשׁ וְלִזְרֹעַ. (2)

וְהָאָרֶץ הַנְּשַׁמָּה תֵּעָבֵד
תַּחַת אֲשֶׁר הָיְתָה שְׁמָמָה.
לִבְנוֹת וְלִנְטֹעַ, לַחֲרשׁ וְלִזְרֹעַ. (2)

SHIR HASHATIL

PLANTER'S SONG

גַּם בָּעִיר, וְגַם בַּכְּפָר

יֶלֶד קוּם יַשְׁכֵּם

וְיֵצֵא לַגַּיְא וְלָהָר,

עִם שְׁתִילִים יְרֻקִּים.

זֶה הַיּוֹם נִטַּע וְנִשְׁתַּל

וְנַכֶּה פֹּה שֹׁרֶשׁ,

עוֹד שָׁנָה וְעוֹד שָׁנָה

וְהִנֵּה פֹּה חֹרֶשׁ.

מקהלה: שִׁירוּ שִׁיר לַשָּׁתִיל

מִיהוּדָה וְעַד הַגָּלִיל!

טַע וּשְׁתֹל, שְׁתֹל וָטַע!

גַּם אֲנִי וְגַם אַתָּה.

150

Hoi, har-ḥi-vu ha-gu-ma   הוֹי, הַרְחִיבוּ הַגּוּמָה

La-ma-tar, la-ḥa-ma!   לַמָּטָר, לַחַמָּה!

Ha-sha-til ha-raḥ yig-dal —   הַשָּׁתִיל הָרַךְ יִגְדַּל—

U-far-ḥa sh'ma-ma.   וּפָרְחָה שְׁמָמָה.

Ma li se-la, ma li hol —   מַה־לִּי סָלַע, מַה־לִּי חוֹל—

Yad v'yad o-de-ret;   יָד וְיָד עוֹדֶרֶת;

Tif ar-tze-nu ha-k'ta-na   תִּיף אַרְצֵנוּ הַקְּטַנָּה

E-retz l'tif-e-ret.   אֶרֶץ לְתִפְאָרֶת.

Purim

PURIM GREETING

Moderato

Won't you o-pen the door for me? Won't you o-pen the door for me? Mish-

lo-ah ma-not I bring to.... you, A Pu-rim song I'll sing to.... you, And I'll

wish you, be-fore I.... leave, Much.... joy this.... Pu-rim.... eve!

THE KING'S SONG

With Spirit

I need a queen, a nice new queen, To sit be-side me on the throne; And
O you are nice, so ve-ry nice! Sweet Es-ther, will you be my bride? So

if she's ve-ry nice in-deed, I'll give her half the things I own.
here's the throne, and half I.....own, And a hund-red and twen-ty lands be-sides.

I've looked at maids, so ma-ny maids With black or red or..... gol-den hair, But

this one shouts, and this one pouts, And so for none of..... these I care

MORDECAI'S PROCESSION

I LOVE THE DAY OF PURIM

I love the day of Pu-rim so!.......... For then, to syn-a-gogue I

go,......... And hear them read the sto-ry old.......... of Esther brave and Ha-man

-bold...... O Pu-rim, O Pu-rim, O Pu-rim full of joy For ev-ery, for ev-ery

Jew-ish girl and boy! Have a par-ty sing a song, Turn the gre-ger loud and long,

Shlo-ah ma-not give and take, Eat your Ho-men-tash-en cake! O Pu-rim, O Pu-rim, O

Pu-rim, full of joy,..... For ev-ery, for ev-ery...... Jew-ish girl and boy......

HAG PURIM

PURIM DAY

Jolly

Hag Pu-rim, hag Pu-rim Hag ga-dol hu la-y'hu-dim. Ma-se-hot,...
Pu-rim day, Pu-rim day, Glad-some, joy-ous ho-li-day. Hap-py throngs,

ra-asha-nim, Z'mi-rot, ri-ku - dim........... Ha-va nar-i-sha Rash, rash, rash.
sing-ing songs, Masked and danc-ing gay.......... Let's make cla-mor, Rah, rah, rah.

Ha-va nar-i-sha Rash, rash, rash. Ha-va nar-i-sha Rash, rash, rash. Ba-ra-a - sha - nim.......
Lus-ty... noi-ses Grah, grah, grah! Loud-ly..... cry and shout hur-ray! With your Gre-gers play.........

Ḥag Pu-rim, ḥag Pu-rim —
Ze el ze shol-ḥim ma-not.
Maḥ-ma-dim, mam-ta-kim,
Tu-fi-nim, mig-da-not.

Purim day, Purim day,
Gladsome, joyous holiday.
Happy throngs, singing songs,
Masked and dancing gay.

חַג פּוּרִים, חַג פּוּרִים —
זֶה אֶל זֶה שׁוֹלְחִים מָנוֹת.
מַחְמַדִּים, מַמְתַּקִּים,
תּוּפִינִים, מִגְדָּנוֹת.

הָבָה נַרְעִישָׁה
רַשׁ, רַשׁ, רַשׁ.
הָבָה נַרְעִישָׁה
רַשׁ, רַשׁ, רַשׁ.
הָבָה נַרְעִישָׁה
רַשׁ, רַשׁ, רַשׁ
בְּרַעֲשָׁנִים.

חַג פּוּרִים, חַג פּוּרִים —
חַג גָּדוֹל הוּא לַיְּהוּדִים,
מַסֵּכוֹת, רַעֲשָׁנִים,
זְמִירוֹת, רְקוּדִים.

ESTHER, IN YOUR GARDEN FAIR

Es-ther in your gar-den fair, Tell... me.. what you dream of there. Do you, in your gar-den bower, Tell your dreams to each sweet flower? "I'm but a child, and in my bower, I like to talk to each sweet flower. And every flow-er, eve-ry tree Is whisp'ring sec-ret things to me."

Esther, Esther, now they bring
   You to stand before the king,
Esther, Esther, now you see —
Queen he chooses you to be!
    "Oh, if he truly does choose me,
    A good and loyal queen I'll be;
    And always, I'll remember too,
    My people, for I am a Jew."

Esther, Esther, queen so great,
Mord'cai's waiting at the gate.
Esther, Esther, great king's wife,
Save, Oh save, your people's life.
    "Oh go, and say to Mordecai:
    'I care not if I live or die —
    If I am queen, or I am a slave —
    My people's life I'll surely save.' "

Moderately fast

1. Oh! once there was a wick-ed wick-ed man, And Ha-man was his
2. And Esth-er was the love-ly queen, of king A-has-u-

name, Sir, He would have mur-dered all the Jews, Tho they were not to blame, Sir;
e-ros, when Ha-man said he'd kill us all, Oh my, how he did scare us;

Refrain

Oh, to-day we'll mer-ry mer-ry be..... Oh, to-day we'll mer-ry mer-ry be......

Oh, to-day we'll mer-ry, mer-ry be And "nash" some Ho-men-tash-en.

The guest of honor he shall be,

This clever Mr. Smarty,

And high above us he shall swing

At a little hanging party.

CHORUS

Of all his cruel and unkind ways

This little joke did cure him.

And don't forget we owe him thanks

For this jolly feast of Purim.

CHORUS

But Mordecai her cousin bold,

Said "What a dreadful *ḥutzpah*,

If guns were but invented now,

This Haman I would shoot, Sir."

CHORUS

When Esther speaking to the king

Of Haman's plot made mention,

"Ha, ha," said he, "Oh, no he won't!

I'll spoil his bad intention."

CHORUS

IN SHU, SHU, SHUSHAN

In a jolly manner

Oh ..... Ha-man was a high and might-y bluff, In Shu-shu Shu-shan long a-

go. .... He .... or-dered Mor-de-cai to take his der-by off In Shu-shu, Shu-shan long a-

go....... So we sing,..... so we sing!..... so we sing and raise a row!....... For

Ha-man he was swing-ing, While Mor de-cai was sing-ing, In Shu-shu shu-shan long a — go..........

But Mordecai sat and laughed in his face

In Shu, Shu, Shushan long ago.

So Haman swore he'd exterminate his race

In Shu, Shu, Shushan long ago.

CHORUS.

O Esther was a timid little maid

In Shu, Shu, Shushan long ago.

But Mordecai told her she needn't be afraid

In Shu, Shu, Shushan long ago.

CHORUS

So she went to the king and she gave him a smile

In Shu, Shu, Shushan long ago.

The king he liked her manner and her style

In Shu, Shu, Shushan long ago.

CHORUS

Ahasuerus was a jolly little king

In Shu, Shu, Shushan long ago.

He ordered Haman to take a little swing

In Shu, Shu, Shushan long ago.

CHORUS

162

ESTHER

Sweetly

I love..... to think of Es — ther, A sim — ple Jew — ish maid,.......
Her mind had then the sweet — ness, Her heart the cou — rage high,.......

When in...... her un — cle's home she lived, And hap — pi — ly..... o — beyed......
That la — ter bade her say "I go, And if...... I die, I die."......

Be — fore she thought of Shu — — shan, It's splen — dor and its gloom,...
Or dreamed her deed of faith might save Her peo — ple from its doom.

FINE

D. C. AL FINE

ZEMER L'PURIM

Ḥav-ra-ya ha-yom Pu-rim, Yom ḥag, sim – ḥa.... la- kol. Ha-va na-

-gil, nis-maḥ V'-ne-tze b'- ma- ḥol............. Nish-kaḥ l'- re- ga kat....

Se-vel u-d'a-got,....... Ma- gal ga- dol na-ase Nir- kod b'li ha-fu- got.....

Ro – nu tza-ha- lu!... Shi – ru ad b'li dai! V'- nar-

Today is Purim, brothers, a happy holiday.
Rejoice and be merry, dance in a ring, turn the
greggers, dance and sing.

חַבְרַיָא, הַיוֹם פּוּרִים,
יוֹם חַג, שִׂמְחָה לַכֹּל.
הָבָה נָגִיל, נִשְׂמַח
וְנֵצֵא בְּמָחוֹל.
נִשְׁכַּח לְרֶגַע קָט
סֵבֶל וּדְאָגוֹת,
מַעְגָּל גָּדוֹל נַעֲשֶׂה
נִרְקֹד בְּלִי הֲפוּגוֹת.

רֹנּוּ, צַהֲלוּ!
שִׁירוּ עַד בְּלִי דָי!
וְנֵרָאֶה לַכֹּל
כִּי עַמֵּנוּ חָי!

Big-dey le-tzan nil-bash,
Ma-se-ḥot al ha-pa-nim.
Ha-sim-ḥa tir-be,
Rik-du ba-not, ba-nim.
Yi-sov ha-ma-gal
V'yaḥ ha-ra-a-shan!
Kol a-sher lo ko-aḥ yesh,
Ya-ke na et Ha-man!
Ro-nu tza-ha-lu . . .

בִּגְדֵי לֵצָן נִלְבַּשׁ,
מַסֵּכוֹת עַל הַפָּנִים.
הַשִּׂמְחָה תִּרְבֶּה,
רִקְדוּ בָּנוֹת, בָּנִים.
יָסֹב הַמַּעְגָּל
וְיַךְ הָרַעֲשָׁן!
כָּל אֲשֶׁר לוֹ כֹחַ יֵשׁ
יַכֶּה נָא אֶת הָמָן!

רֹנּוּ, צַהֲלוּ! . . .

ZE HAYOM

THIS IS PURIM, FELLOWS

Ha-man ben Ham-da-ta
Ra-sha hu, kol bo,
V'ri-bon kol ha-o-lam
N'ka-ma a-sa vo,
Z'ḥor Ha-man, z'ḥor,
Na-fal-ta ba-bor,
Ki ni-sim a-sa la-nu El.
Uv'ḥen pit-ḥu pe,
Un-za-mer shir ze,
Un-ra ked ko yo-mam va-lel.

Haman, wicked schemer,
His kind we've always known.
But God, the great Redeemer,
These fiends has overthrown.
Wait, Haman, Oh wait,
Decreed is your fate,
Avenging and swift is His rod!
Dance children, and sing,
Make larger your ring,
In happy thanksgiving to God.

זֶה הַיּוֹם יוֹם פּוּרִים,
מַה נָּעִים וּמַה טּוֹב,
זְמִירוֹת נְזַמֵּרָה
וְנִשְׂמַח עַד אֵין סוֹף.
שְׂמַח, מָרְדְּכַי, שְׂמַח,
הַצָּרוֹת נָא שְׁכַח,
לָנֶצַח לֹא נִשְׁכַּח הַנֵּס.
הוֹי שִׁירוּ נָא שִׁיר,
כִּי בְּשׁוּשַׁן הָעִיר
הָמָן הָאֲגָגִי אָז מֵת.

הָמָן בֶּן הַמְדָתָא
רָשָׁע הוּא, כָּל בּוֹ,
וְרִבּוֹן כָּל הָעוֹלָם
נְקָמָה עָשָׂה בוֹ.
זְכֹר, הָמָן, זְכֹר,
נָפַלְתָּ בַּבּוֹר,
כִּי נִסִּים עָשָׂה לָנוּ אֵל.
וּבְכֵן פִּתְחוּ פֶּה,
וּנְזַמֵּר שִׁיר זֶה,
וּנְרַקֵּד כֹּה יוֹמָם וָלֵיל.

UTZU ETZA

עוּצוּ עֵצָה וְתֻפָר.

דַּבְּרוּ דָבָר וְלֹא יָקוּם.

כִּי עִמָּנוּ אֵל.

You may scheme and plot against us, but to no
avail. For God is with us.

FOR PURIM

Oh, Ha-man lived in Shu-shan town, And he was most op-pres-sive; He wore a blue and pur-ple hat, Three cor-nered and im-pres-sive, three cor-nered and im-pres-sive. Knock ye, knock-ers, knock, knock, knock. And rat-tlers rat-tle, rat-tle on......... This is our Pu-rim ho-li-day, A

day of joy and fun, fun, fun, A day of joy and fun.

With Mordecai was Haman grieved
    And swore in his vexation
To hang him on the gallows high,
    And wipe out all his nation. (2)
                CHORUS

But on that day a miracle
    God wrought, and sent salvation,
For we were saved, but Haman was
    Effaced from God's creation. (2)
                CHORUS

He sent out letters: "Rise and slay
    The Jews that they all perish,
The thirteenth day of *Adar*-month," —
    The Purim-day we cherish. (2)
                CHORUS

In memory of the cornered hat
    Of Haman so ambitious,
We eat a cake resembling it,
    A *Homentash* delicious. (2)
                CHORUS

SHOSHANAS YA'AKOV

Sho - sha-nas ya - a - kov .... tzo-ho-lo v'-so-me — ho ...... Bir-o-som ya — a-

had........ t' – ḥe – les Mor – d – ḥai........ Sho – ḥe – les Mor – d – ḥai...........

T'shu-o – som ho – yi – so lo – ne – tzaḥ V'-sik-vo – som b'ḥol dor vo – dor......... L'-

ho – di – a she – kol ko – ve – ḥo Lo...... ye – vo – shu v – lo yi – kol – mu Sho-

Orur Ho – mon a-sher bi – kesh t'– ab-di Boruḥ Mor-d-ḥai........ ha – y' – ḥu – di

שׁוֹשַׁנַּת יַעֲקֹב צָהֲלָה וְשָׂמֵחָה
בִּרְאוֹתָם יַחַד תְּכֵלֶת מָרְדְּכָי.
תְּשׁוּעָתָם הָיִיתָ לָנֶצַח
וְתִקְוָתָם בְּכָל דּוֹר וָדוֹר.
לְהוֹדִיעַ שֶׁכָּל קֹוֶיךָ
לֹא יֵבֹשׁוּ וְלֹא יִכָּלְמוּ.
שׁוֹשַׁנַּת . . . .

אָרוּר הָמָן אֲשֶׁר בִּקֵּשׁ לְאַבְּדִי
בָּרוּךְ מָרְדְּכַי הַיְּהוּדִי.
אֲרוּרָה זֶרֶשׁ אֵשֶׁת מַפְחִידִי
בְּרוּכָה אֶסְתֵּר בַּעֲדִי.
שׁוֹשַׁנַּת . . . .

אֲרוּרִים כָּל הָרְשָׁעִים
בְּרוּכִים כָּל הַצַּדִּיקִים.
וְגַם חַרְבוֹנָה זָכוּר לַטּוֹב.
שׁוֹשַׁנַת . . . .

KIDDUSH

vo-nu vo-har-to v'-o-so-nu ki-dash-to mi - kol ho - a — mim (v' sha-bos) u-mo-a-dey... kod-she-ho ... (b'-

a-ha-vo uv-ro-tzon) b'-sim-koh uv'-so-son hin-hal-to — nu: Bo-ruh a—to A-do-noi m'-ka-

desh(ha-sha-bos v'-Yisro-el v'haz-ma-nim.) Bo-ruh a-to A-do-noi e-lo-hey-nu me-leh ho-o-lom, she-
Yis-ro-el v'-haz-ma - - nim:

-he-he-yo—nu.... v'-ki-mo—nu. v'-hi-gi-o-nu laz - - - man ha - ze.

סַבְרִי מָרָנָן וְרַבּוֹתַי

בָּרוּךְ אַתָּה יְיָ, אֱלֹהֵינוּ מֶלֶךְ הָעוֹלָם, בּוֹרֵא פְּרִי הַגָּפֶן:

בָּרוּךְ אַתָּה יְיָ, אֱלֹהֵינוּ מֶלֶךְ הָעוֹלָם, אֲשֶׁר בָּחַר בָּנוּ מִכָּל-עָם, וְרוֹמְמָנוּ מִכָּל-
לָשׁוֹן, וְקִדְּשָׁנוּ בְּמִצְוֹתָיו. וַתִּתֶּן לָנוּ יְיָ אֱלֹהֵינוּ בְּאַהֲבָה (לשבת שַׁבָּתוֹת לִמְנוּחָה וּ) מוֹעֲדִים
לְשִׂמְחָה, חַגִּים וּזְמַנִּים לְשָׂשׂוֹן אֶת יוֹם (לשבת הַשַּׁבָּת הַזֶּה, וְאֶת יוֹם) חַג הַמַּצּוֹת הַזֶּה.
זְמַן חֵרוּתֵנוּ (לשבת בְּאַהֲבָה) מִקְרָא קֹדֶשׁ, זֵכֶר לִיצִיאַת מִצְרָיִם. כִּי בָנוּ בָחַרְתָּ וְאוֹתָנוּ
קִדַּשְׁתָּ מִכָּל הָעַמִּים (וְשַׁבָּת) וּמוֹעֲדֵי קָדְשֶׁךָ (בְּאַהֲבָה וּבְרָצוֹן) בְּשִׂמְחָה וּבְשָׂשׂוֹן
הִנְחַלְתָּנוּ: בָּרוּךְ אַתָּה יְיָ מְקַדֵּשׁ (הַשַּׁבָּת וְ) יִשְׂרָאֵל וְהַזְּמַנִּים:

בָּרוּךְ אַתָּה אֲדֹנָי, אֱלֹהֵינוּ מֶלֶךְ הָעוֹלָם, שֶׁהֶחֱיָנוּ וְקִיְּמָנוּ וְהִגִּיעָנוּ לַזְּמַן הַזֶּה.

MA NISHTANO

Ma nish-ta-no ha-lai-lo ha—ze.... mi-kol ha-le — los? .... She-b'-

1 -hol ha-le-los.... o-nu oh — lin.. ho-metz u — ma-tzo,.... ha-
2 -hol ha-le-los.... o-nu oh — lin.. sh'-or.. y'— ro-kos,.... ha-
3 -hol ha-le-los en o-nu mat-bi-lin...... a — fi-lu pa-am e — hos,.... ha-
4 -hol ha-le-los..... o-nu oh — lin ben yosh-vin u — ven m'-su-bin,.... ha-

1 -lai-lo ha-ze, ku — lo.....ma-tzo. She-b'— ror......... She-b'-
2 -lai-lo ha-ze, mo— She-b'—
3 -lai-lo ha-ze, sh'—
4 -lai-lo ha-ze, ku—

tey f'-o — mim......... She-b'— lo-nu m'-su—bin.........

Why is this night different from all other nights?
On this night we eat Matzah and bitter herbs; we
dip parsley in salt water and horseradish in ḥaroset;
and we recline at the table as we eat.

מַה נִּשְׁתַּנָּה הַלַּיְלָה הַזֶּה מִכָּל
הַלֵּילוֹת?

שֶׁבְּכָל הַלֵּילוֹת אָנוּ אוֹכְלִין חָמֵץ
וּמַצָּה, הַלַּיְלָה הַזֶּה כֻּלּוֹ מַצָּה.

שֶׁבְּכָל הַלֵּילוֹת אָנוּ אוֹכְלִין שְׁאָר
יְרָקוֹת, הַלַּיְלָה הַזֶּה מָרוֹר.

שֶׁבְּכָל הַלֵּילוֹת אֵין אָנוּ מַטְבִּילִין
אֲפִילוּ פַּעַם אֶחָת, הַלַּיְלָה הַזֶּה
שְׁתֵּי פְעָמִים.

שֶׁבְּכָל הַלֵּילוֹת אָנוּ אוֹכְלִין בֵּין
יוֹשְׁבִין וּבֵין מְסֻבִּין, הַלַּיְלָה הַזֶּה
כֻּלָּנוּ מְסֻבִּין.

Joyously

A-vo-dim ho-yi-nu..... ho-yi-nu, a — to b'-ney ho-rin... b'-ney ho-rin.

A-vo-dim..... ho — yi-nu, a-to, a-to b'-ney ho-rin......

A-vo-dim...... ho — yi-nu, a-to, a-to b'-ney ho-rin, b'-ney ho-rin.

עֲבָדִים הָיִינוּ, עַתָּה בְּנֵי חוֹרִין.

Once we were slaves. Today we are free men.

Today we are free men.

V'HI SHE'OMDO

-ha-lo-se-nu. V'ha-ko-dosh bo-ruḥ hu... ma-tzi-le-nu... ma-tzi-le-nu

mi-yo-dom v'-hi she-om---do.....la-avo-sey-nu v'-lo-nu.-----

God's faithfulness to our fathers and to us has
ever saved us from those who rose up against us to
destroy us.

וְהִיא שֶׁעָמְדָה לַאֲבוֹתֵינוּ וְלֶנוּ.
שֶׁלֹּא אֶחָד בִּלְבַד עָמַד עָלֵינוּ
לְכַלּוֹתֵנוּ. (אֶלָּא שֶׁבְּכָל דּוֹר וָדוֹר,
עוֹמְדִים עָלֵינוּ לְכַלּוֹתֵנוּ.) וְהַקָּדוֹשׁ
בָּרוּךְ הוּא מַצִּילֵנוּ מִיָּדָם:

179

DAYENU

Rhythmically

I – lu ho-tzi, ho-tzi-o – nu,   ho-tzi-o – nu mi-Mitz-ra-yim,

ho-tzi-o – nu mi-mitz-ra-yim, Da – ye — nu: I – lu ho-tzi, ho-tzi-o – nu,

ho-tzi-o – nu mi-Mitz-ra – yim,   ho-tzi-o – nu mi-Mitz-ra – yim,

Da — ye — nu:..........   Da-da-ye-nu.....   da-da-ye-nu.......

da-da-ye-nu   da - ye-nu da-ye-nu........   -ye-nu da-ye-nu.

I-lu no-san lo-nu es ha-Sha-bos, Da-ye-nu:

I-lu no-san lo-nu es ha-To-roh, Da-ye-nu:

I-lu hiḥ-ni-so-nu l'E-retz Yis-ro-el, Da-ye-nu:

אֵלּוּ הוֹצִיאָנוּ מִמִּצְרַיִם, דַּיֵּנוּ:

אֵלּוּ נָתַן לָנוּ אֶת הַשַּׁבָּת, דַּיֵּנוּ:

אֵלּוּ נָתַן לָנוּ אֶת הַתּוֹרָה, דַּיֵּנוּ:

אֵלּוּ הִכְנִיסָנוּ לְאֶרֶץ יִשְׂרָאֵל, דַּיֵּנוּ:

Had He done nothing more than take us out of Egypt, for that alone, we should have been grateful. Had He given us the Sabbath and nothing more, Dayenu. Had He brought us into the land of Israel, Dayenu!

HALELUYOH

Rhythmically

Ha-le-lu-yoh, ha-le-lu-yoh   Ha - le - lu........ av-dey A-do - noi...........
y'-hee   shem A-do-noy m'vo - roh...........

Ha-le-tu-yoh, ha-le-tu-yoh Ha-le-lu es shem A-do-noi........
Me-a to v'-ad....... o-lom.........

Ha-le-tu-yoh..... ha-le-tu-yoh, ha-le-tu-yoh, ha-le-tu-yoh,

Ha-le-tu-yoh...... ha-le-tu-yoh, ha-le-tu-yoh ha-le-tu-yoh.

Ha-le-lu-yoh, ha-le-lu-yoh

M'ki-mi me-o-for dol.

Ha-le-lu-yoh, ha-le-lu-yoh

Me-ash-pos yo-rim ev-yon.

Ha-le-lu yoh.

הַלְלוּיָה, הַלְלוּיָה

מְקִימִי מֵעָפָר דָּל.

הַלְלוּיָה, הַלְלוּיָה

מֵאַשְׁפֹּת יָרִים אֶבְיוֹן.

הַלְלוּיָה.

הַלְלוּיָה, הַלְלוּיָה

הַלְלוּ עַבְדֵי אֲדֹנָי.

הַלְלוּיָה, הַלְלוּיָה

הַלְלוּ אֶת שֵׁם אֲדֹנָי.

הַלְלוּיָה.

הַלְלוּיָה, הַלְלוּיָה

יְהִי שֵׁם אֲדֹנָי מְבֹרָךְ.

הַלְלוּיָה, הַלְלוּיָה,

מֵעַתָּה וְעַד עוֹלָם.

הַלְלוּיָה.

Haleluyah, Haleluyah,

Sing ye servants of the Lord.

Tell His goodness, glory and might.

Proclaim His living word.

    Haleluyah.

Haleluyah, Haleluyah,

Praise God forever more.

A rock and refuge is He to us

Now as in days of yore.

    Haleluyah.

ELIYOHU HANOVI

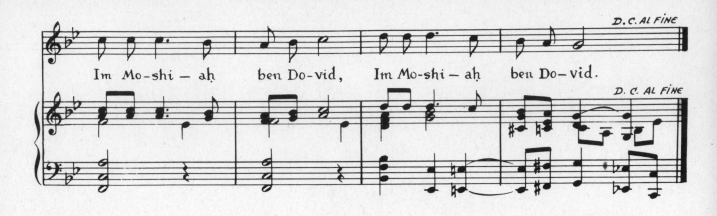

Im Mo-shi – aḥ   ben Do-vid,   Im Mo-shi – aḥ   ben Do-vid.

May the prophet Elijah come soon, in our time,
with the Messiah, son of David.

בְּמְהֵרָה בְיָמֵינוּ   אֵלִיָהוּ הַנָבִיא

יָבֹא אֵלֵינוּ   אֵלִיָהוּ הַתִּשְׁבִּי

עִם מָשִׁיחַ בֶּן דָוִד,   אֵלִיָהוּ, אֵלִיָהוּ,

עִם מָשִׁיחַ בֶּן דָוִד.   אֵלִיָהוּ הַגִלְעָדִי.

ADIR BIMLUḤO

With joy

A – dir … bi – m'lu-ḥo … bo – hur ka-ha – lo-ḥo. …
Do – gul … bi – m'lu-ḥo … ho – dur ka-ha – lo-ḥo. …

G'du – dov … yom-ru lo: L'– ḥo … u – l'– ḥo … L'–
Vosi – kov …

ho..... ki.... l'—ho......... L'—ho..... af .. l'—ho......... L'—

CHORUS

ho... A-do-noi ha-mam-lo-ho ki lo no—e... ki lo yo—e.

Powerful in His sovereignty, glorious, supreme. His hosts say to Him: to Thee, to Thee alone is sovereignty. For to Him all praise is meet.

אַדִּיר בִּמְלוּכָה בָּחוּר כַּהֲלָכָה.
גְּדוּדָיו יֹאמְרוּ לוֹ:

לְךָ וּלְךָ, לְךָ כִּי לְךָ.
לְךָ אַף לְךָ. לְךָ אֲדֹנָי הַמַּמְלָכָה
כִּי לוֹ נָאֶה כִּי לוֹ יָאֶה.

דָּגוּל בִּמְלוּכָה הָדוּר כַּהֲלָכָה.
וָתִיקָיו יֹאמְרוּ לוֹ:
לְךָ וּלְךָ . . .

Za-kai bi-m'lu-ho ho-sin ka-halo-ho.
Taf-s'rov yom-ru lo:
  L'ho u-l'ho . . . .

זַכַּאי בִּמְלוּכָה חָסִין כַּהֲלָכָה.
טַפְסְרָיו יֹאמְרוּ לוֹ:
לְךָ וּלְךָ . . .

ADIR HU

PRAISE THE LORD

Slowly, with vigor

A-dir hu, A-dir hu. Yiv-ne ve-so b'ko-rov. Bim-hey-ro......, bim-hey-ro.....
Praise the Lord! One ac-cord, Sound throughout cre-a-tion; Laud and sing........ hon-or bring

b'yo-mey-nu b'-ko-rov. El b'-ney, El b'-ney B'ney ves-ho b'-ko-rov.
Him with-out ces-sa-tion; And His fame loud pro-claim, Eve-'ry land and na-tion.

Bo-ḥur hu, go-dol hu.	בָּחוּר הוּא, נָּדוֹל הוּא.	אַדִּיר הוּא, אַדִּיר הוּא.
yivne . . . . . . יבנה		יִבְנֶה בֵיתוֹ בְּקָרוֹב.
Do-gul hu, ho-dur hu.	דָּגוּל הוּא, הָדוּר הוּא.	בִּמְהֵרָה, בִּמְהֵרָה,
yivne . . . . . . יבנה		בְּיָמֵינוּ בְּקָרוֹב.
Vo-sik hu, za-kai hu.	וָתִיק הוּא, זַכַּאי הוּא.	אֵל בְּנֵה, אֵל בְּנֵה
yivne . . . . . . יבנה		בְּנֵה בֵיתְךָ בְּקָרוֹב.
Ḥo-sid hu, to-hor hu	חָסִיד הוּא, טָהוֹר הוּא.	
yivne . . . . . . יבנה		
Yo-ḥid hu, ka-bir hu.	יָחִיד הוּא, כַּבִּיר הוּא.	
yivne . . . . . . יבנה		

Lo! The spring joy doth bring,
    Winter's frosts are ended;
Gladness reigns, life remains,
    With sweet pleasure blended;
God doth bear what His care
    And His love defended.

Father, we pray to Thee,
    Let Thy grace be o'er us;
Let Thy light, and Thy might
    Show the paths before us;
Ours Thy love, from above,
    And Thy grace which bore us.

Next year may we be in Jerusalem.

לְשָׁנָה הַבָּאָה בִּירוּשָׁלַיִם.

EḤOD MI YODE'A

WHO WILL SING ME?

Sh'na-yim mi yo-de-a?
Sh'na-yim ani yo-de-a.
*Sh'ney lu-ḥos ha-b'ris
E-ḥod Elo-hey-nu
She-ba-sho-ma-yim u-vo-o-retz

Sh'lo-sho mi yo-de-a?
Sh'lo-sho ani yo-de-a.
*Sh'lo-sho o-vos,
*Sh'ney lu-ḥos ha-b'ris
E-ḥod Elo-hey-nu
She-ba-sho-ma-yim u-vo-o-retz.

Ar-ba mi yo-de-a?
Ar-ba ani yo-de-a.
*Ar-ba i-mo-hos,
*Sh'lo-sho o-vos,
*Sh'ney lu-ḥos ha-b'ris
E-ḥod Elo-hey-nu
She-ba-sho-ma-yim u-vo-o-retz.

Who will sing me of the number Two?
I will sing you of the number Two.
Two tablets of the Law,
One for Almighty God
Who reigns in heaven and upon the earth.

Who will sing me of the number Three?
I will sing you of the number Three.
Three for the patriarchs,
Two tablets of the Law,
One for Almighty God
Who reigns in heaven and upon the earth.

Four for the matriarchs,
Five for the Pentateuch,
Six days creation,
Seven days are in the week,
Eight lights of Ḥanukah,
Nine for the festivals,
Ten for the Commandments,
Eleven stars in Joseph's dream,
Twelve tribes of Israel,
Thirteen attributes of God.

אַרְבַּע מִי יוֹדֵעַ?
אַרְבַּע אֲנִי יוֹדֵעַ.
*אַרְבַּע אִמָּהוֹת,
שְׁלֹשָׁה אָבוֹת,
שְׁנֵי לוּחוֹת הַבְּרִית,
אֶחָד אֱלֹהֵינוּ
שֶׁבַּשָּׁמַיִם וּבָאָרֶץ.

שְׁלֹשָׁה מִי יוֹדֵעַ?
שְׁלֹשָׁה אֲנִי יוֹדֵעַ.
*שְׁלֹשָׁה אָבוֹת,
שְׁנֵי לוּחוֹת הַבְּרִית,
אֶחָד אֱלֹהֵינוּ
שֶׁבַּשָּׁמַיִם וּבָאָרֶץ.

שְׁנַיִם מִי יוֹדֵעַ?
שְׁנַיִם אֲנִי יוֹדֵעַ.
*שְׁנֵי לוּחוֹת הַבְּרִית,
אֶחָד אֱלֹהֵינוּ
שֶׁבַּשָּׁמַיִם וּבָאָרֶץ.

אֶחָד מִי יוֹדֵעַ?
אֶחָד אֲנִי יוֹדֵעַ.
אֶחָד אֱלֹהֵינוּ
שֶׁבַּשָּׁמַיִם וּבָאָרֶץ.

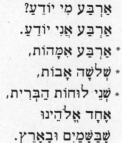

Sing these lines to the music of the second measure, second line, repeating the same music for each succeeding number. Then repeat the music again with the words ECHAD ELO-HEY-NU, and continue with rest of song.

ḤAD GADYO

Moderato

Had Gad – yo,.............. Had Gad – yo.... D' – za-bin a-bo

bis – rey.... zu-zey Had Gad – yo....................... had gad – yo.

V' – – o-so shun-ro v'o – hal l'-gad-yo (...................................) D' –
V' – – o-so kal-bo v'no – shah l'-shun-ro D' – o –hal l'-gad – yo,

* *This phrase ( ) to be omitted the first time*

-za-bin a-bo.... bis – re..... zu-zey Had gad – yo...............

190

had gad - yo........ V' - - o-so ḥut-ro vhi-ko l'-ḥal-bo

(* PHRASE A

(* PHRASE B

D' - no-shaḥ l'-shun - ro........ D' - o-ḥal l'-gad - yo.

D'ZABIN ABU

* Phrase A and Phrase B to be added alternately as new phrases appear with each new stanza.

*My father bought an only kid for two zuzim. A
cat came and ate the kid; a dog came and bit the
cat; a stick came and beat the dog; a fire came and
burned the stick; water came and quenched the fire
... an only kid, my father bought for two zuzim.*

חַד גַּדְיָא, חַד גַּדְיָא.

דְּזַבִּין אַבָּא בִּתְרֵי זוּזֵי
חַד גַּדְיָא, חַד גַּדְיָא.

וְאָתָא שׁוּנְרָא וְאָכַל לְגַדְיָא.
דזבין ...

וְאָתָא כַלְבָּא וְנָשַׁךְ לְשׁוּנְרָא
דְּאָכַל לְגַדְיָא.
דזבין ...

וְאָתָא חוּטְרָא וְהִכָּה לְכַלְבָּא.
דְּנָשַׁךְ לְשׁוּנְרָא דְּאָכַל לְגַדְיָא.
דזבין ...

וְאָתָא נוּרָא וְשָׂרַף לְחוּטְרָא
דְּהִכָּה לְכַלְבָּא, דְּנָשַׁךְ לְשׁוּנְרָא
דְּאָכַל לְגַדְיָא.
דזבין ...

V'o-so nu-ro v'so-raf l'ḥut-ro
D'hi-ko l'ḥal-bo, d'no-shaḥ l'shun-ro,
D'o-ḥal l'gad-yo.

D'za-bin ...

191

V'o-so ma-yo v'ho-vo l'nu-ro

וְאָתָא מַיָא וְכָבָה לְנוּרָא

D'so-raf l'hut-ro, d'hi-ko l'hal-bo,

דְּשָׂרַף לְחוּטְרָא, דְּהִכָּה לְכַלְבָּא,

D'no-shah l'shun-ro,

דְּנָשַׁךְ לְשׁוּנְרָא דְּאָכַל לְגַדְיָא.

D'o-hal l'gad-yo.

D'za-bin . . .

דזבין . . .

V'o-so ha-ko-dosh bo-ruh hu,

וְאָתָא הַקָּדוֹשׁ בָּרוּךְ הוּא,

V'sho-hat l'ma-lah ha-mo-
ves, d'sho-hat l'sho-het,

וְשָׁחַט לְמַלְאַךְ הַמָּוֶת, דְּשָׁחַט לְשׁוֹחֵט,

D'sho-hat l'so-ro, d'sho-so l'ma-yo,

דְּשָׁחַט לְתוֹרָא, דְּשָׁתָא לְמַיָא,

D'ho-vo l'nu-ro, d'so-raf l'hut-ro,

דְּכָבָה לְנוּרָא, דְּשָׂרַף לְחוּטְרָא,

D'hi-ko l'hal-bo, d'no-shah l'shun-ro,

דְּהִכָּה לְכַלְבָּא, דְּנָשַׁךְ לְשׁוּנְרָא,

D'o-hal l'gad-yo,

דְּאָכַל לְגַדְיָא, דְּזַבִּין אַבָּא בִּתְרֵי

D'za-bin a-bo bis-rey zu-zey.

זוּזֵי.

Had gad-yo, had gad-yo.

חַד גַּדְיָא, חַד גַּדְיָא.

CONCERNING A KID

With spirit

CHORUS

Had gad-yo.......... had gad-yo........ Had gad-yo........... had gad-yo.....

FINE

SOLO

Oh, grand-pa went to mar-ket once To see what he could buy; He bought a snow-white kid be-cause It caught and held his eye. The cru-el cat, the gree-dy cat, With-in a val-ley hid, And then jumped out; with wick-ed claws He slew the lit-tle kid.

D. C. AL FINE

The dog was angry with the cat
For doing such a deed.
He leaped upon the frightened cat;
He slew him with great speed.
The stick was very angry then,
And leaped up from his place;
He beat the dog upon the head,
And even on the face.

CHORUS

The fire gave an angry roar,
And leaped to the attack;
It burned the stick and left it there
Like ashes, crisp and black.
The water saw the burning flame,
And flowed all round about;
It covered every single spark,
And put the fire out.

CHORUS

193

The thirsty ox from pasture came,
And saw the water there;
He drank up every single drop;
Not one drop did he spare.
The butcher came and saw the ox;
He firmly bound his feet.
Then with his knife he slew the ox,
Because he needed meat.

CHORUS

Then came the angel dark of death,
With his ten thousand eyes;
He merely looked — the butcher fell;
A heap of bones he lies.
Then God an angel sent to strike
The messenger of death;
The angel bright blew just one puff,
And slew him with his breath.

CHORUS

ESH'ALO ELOHIM

YEMENITE SONG

With accent

Esh - a - la E - lo - him, yig-a - la sh' - vu - yim
Sway-ing..... and pray-ing Ex - iles..... to their land re-turn.

Esh - a - la E - lo - him, yig-a - la sh' - vu - yim.....
Sway-ing... and pray - ing Ex - iles...... to their land re - turn. From

Ye — e—sof z'—ru — im, ye—e—sof z'—ru— im... Ra—ha—man ra—hem....

East and West and South and North, Lead them Thou our Fa-ther, forth, God of Is—ra—el....

Na-a-le l'ar-tze-nu, b'shi-ra v'zim-ra (2)

Uv'kol ri-na, uv'kol ri-na

Ra-ḥa-man ra-ḥem.

Swinging and singing

Into their land they come.

Swinging and singing

Into their land they come.

Hearts aglow,

And voices ringing;

First fruits of their labors bringing,

God of Israel.

אֶשְׁאֲלָה אֱלֹהִים, יִגְאֲלָה שְׁבוּיִים (2)

יְאֱסֹף זְרוּעִים, יְאֱסֹף זְרוּעִים,

רַחֲמָן רַחֵם.

נַעֲלָה לְאַרְצֵנוּ, בִּשִׁירָה וְזִמְרָה (2)

וּבְקוֹל רִנָּה, וּבְקוֹל רִנָּה,

רַחֲמָן רַחֵם.

TO THE RED SEA

March time

To the Red sea, the... Red Sea, The new free men... are...

go - - - - ing To the Red Sea, ... the ...... Red Sea, ... Where

wind and wave are blow - ing, To the Red Sea .... the Red Sea .... Where

strong waves wild-ly ... toss, ... But God .... shall work a mir-a-cle, And

all .. the Jews shall cross, shall cross ;   all .. the Jews shall cross, shall cross.

Lag Ba'omer

HAYA'ARA

TODAY'S LAG BA'OMER

With Swing

mea - dow, the mea-dow, now ga-ther and go, And

Ha - - - ya - ra, ha-ya-ra b'- ke-shet va-hetz, Na-
To the mea-dow, the..... mea-dow, with... ar-row and bow, Come,

take in your hands both the ar-row and bow, And...... fall on the "foe-men," and

-vo-a sa-de, sham ben pe-rah va-netz, Sham..... ye-rek v'-tzi-por v'-
child-ren, we'll go where the flow-ers all grow, Where there's grass and there's bright-ness as

shoot down your "foe," To - - day's Lag B'- o-mer, Lag B'o-mer's to-day.

-ra-hav en ketz, Ha - yom Lag B'- o-mer, Lag - B'o-mer ha-yom.
far as you go. To - day's Lag B'- o-mer, Lag B'o-mer's to-day.

FINE

197

Mi sa - viv.............ah gil, ur - na - nim sham u - fo, Ha -
There the grass-hop-per chirps, and there buz-zes the fly, And the

i - ru v'ney ho - fesh, ha - ri - u ho, ho Y' - ru va - ley hetz.....va -
frogs in the ru-shes jump e - ver so high, And the lit - tle birds chir-rup; Cheep,

- ro - vu "Pi fo" Ha - yom Lag B'o - mer, Lag B'o - mer ha - yom. Ha -
cheep", they all cry. To - day's Lag B'o - mer, Lag B'o - mer's to-day. To the

D.C. AL FINE

הַיַעְרָה, הַיַעְרָה, בְּקֶשֶׁת וָחֵץ,
נָבוֹאָה שָׂדֶה, שָׁם בֵּין פֶּרַח וָנֵץ,
שָׁם יֶרֶק וְצִפּוֹר וְרַחַב אֵין קֵץ,
הַיּוֹם ל"ג בָּעֹמֶר, ל"ג בָּעֹמֶר הַיּוֹם. (2).

מִסָּבִיב אַף גִּיל, וְרִנָּנִים שָׁם וּפֹה,
הֵעִירוּ בְּנֵי חֹפֶשׁ, הָרִיעוּ הוֹ הוֹ,
יָרוּ בַּעֲלֵי הֵץ וְרֹבוּ "פִּי פֹּו"
הַיּוֹם ל"ג בָּעֹמֶר, ל"ג בָּעֹמֶר הַיּוֹם. (2).

198

ON JUDAH'S HILLS

Hu m'ḥa-lel, ko-rey sha-lom:

E-lai, e-lai g'shu ha-lom!

Yesh man-gi-not b'fi ḥa-lil,

Yesh a-ga-dot po va-Ga-lil.

    Lee, lee, lee . . . .

Ha-yo ha-ya gi-bor a-tik.

Tzu-rim ba-ka, s'la-im he-tik.

B'shir ḥa-yim ya-tza lak-rav

Mul a-saf-suf ga-dol va-rav

    Lee, lee, lee . . . .

Upon his flute he sings a greeting,

To romping goats and lambs ableating;

The soft yet moving notes relate,

Old hero tales — Judea's fate.

    Lee, lee, lee . . . .

A man there was, so strong and bold,

Could uproot trees, crush boulders old;

With song on lips went forth to war

For Israel, in days of yore.

    Lee, lee, lee . . . .

"Tov la-mut al ha-mish-mar
B'ad ar-tze-nu" — ko a-mar.
Ha-yo ha-ya gi-bor hi-da,
Lo z'ro-a y'hida.

    Lee, lee, lee . . . .

From Bethar's walls with foes he vied;
Long years the enemies defied,
His people's freedom to defend;
And battling thus he met his end.

    Lee, lee, lee . . . .

הָיֹה הָיָה גִּבּוֹר עַתִּיק.
צוּרִים בָּקַע, סְלָעִים הֶעָתִּיק.
בְּשִׁיר חַיִּים יָצָא לַקְרָב
מוּל אֲסַפְסוּף גָּדוֹל וָרָב.
לִי־לִי־לִי . . .

עָלַי גִּבְעָה שָׁם בַּגָּלִיל,
יוֹשֵׁב שׁוֹמֵר וּבְפִיו חָלִיל.
הוּא מְחַלֵּל שִׁירַת רוֹעֶה
לַשֶּׂה, לַגְּדִי, לְשִׂיחַ תּוֹעֶה.
לִי־לִי־לִי . . .

„טוֹב לָמוּת עַל הַמִּשְׁמָר
בְּעַד אַרְצֵנוּ" – כֹּה אָמָר.
הָיֹה הָיָה גִּבּוֹר־חִידָה,
לוֹ זְרוֹעַ־יְחִידָה.
לִי־לִי־לִי . . .

הוּא מְחַלֵּל, קוֹרֵא שָׁלוֹם:
אֵלַי, אֵלַי, גְּשׁוּ הֲלֹם!
יֵשׁ מַנְגִּינוֹת בְּפִי חָלִיל,
יֵשׁ אַגָּדוֹת פֹּה בַּגָּלִיל.
לִי־לִי־לִי . . .

BAR KOHBA

Om'rim: No - lad ben ha - k'ru - vim........... Mi-sh'mey ma - rom Ya-

rod ya - rad........ B'-yom ba - hir Nif - la...... e - had B'yom ba-

hir Nif-la e - ḥad....... Bi-z'ro-a oz Ey - tzim a - kar,...........

V'-yesh o - m'rim:Gam etz, gam har....... Gi-bor ha - ya Ben ko - ha-

vim, ... Om'-rim: Od ḥai Hu ben kru-vim. ....

Va-y'hi ha-yom —	וַיְהִי הַיּוֹם—	גִּבּוֹר הָיָה
A-saf ha-am	אָסַף הָעָם,	בֶּן־כּוֹכָבִים,
U-va-o-yev	וּבָאוֹיֵב	אוֹמְרִים: נוֹלַד
Nil-ḥam, nil-ḥam.	נִלְחָם, נִלְחָם.	בֵּין הַכְּרוּבִים.
Nil-ḥam ba-yom,	נִלְחָם בַּיּוֹם,	מִשְּׁמֵי־מָרוֹם
Nil-ḥam ba-leyl —	נִלְחָם בַּלֵּיל—	יָרַד יָרַד
Li-v'ney a-mo	לִבְנֵי עַמּוֹ	בְּיוֹם בָּהִיר,
Ha-ya go-el.	הָיָה גּוֹאֵל.	נִפְלָא אֶחָד.
Va-y'hi ha-yom —	וַיְהִי הַיּוֹם—	בִּזְרוֹעַ־עָז
Na-fal ḥa-lal.	נָפַל חָלָל.	עֵצִים עָקַר,
Na-fal gi-bor —	נָפַל גִּבּוֹר—	וְיֵשׁ אוֹמְרִים:
Ḥa-val, ḥa-val!	חֲבָל, חֲבָל!	גַּם עֵץ, גַּם הָר.
Gi-bor ha-ya	גִּבּוֹר הָיָה	
Ben ko-ḥa-vim.	בֶּן־כּוֹכָבִים.	
O-m'rim: Od ḥai	אוֹמְרִים: עוֹד חַי	
Hu ben kru-vim . . .	הוּא בֵּין כְּרוּבִים . . .	

Men say, he was the son of the stars who descended to earth, one glorious day. He fought the foe and redeemed his people, then fell, alas! But he lives on, they say, among the cherubs where he was born.

BAR YOḤAI

בַּר יוֹחָאִי, בַּר יוֹחָאִי,
בַּר יוֹחָאִי, אַשְׁרֶיךָ.
שֶׁמֶן טוֹב, שֶׁמֶן שָׂשׂוֹן
נִמְשַׁחְתָּ מֵחֲבֵרֶיךָ.

Bar Yoḥai, fortunate are you, for you were chosen
to be anointed from among your peers.

TO FETCH THE TORAH DOWN

Trippingly

The.... an-gels came a-mus-ter-ing, A-mus-ter-ing, a-

mus-ter-ing, The..... an-gels came... a-clus-ter-ing, A-

round the sap-phire throne. A-ques-tion-ing of one an-other, Of one an-o-ther, of

one an-o-ther, A - ques-tion-ing each one his... bro-ther A - round the sap-phire throne.

Pray who is he, and where is he,
And where is he, and where is he,
Who shining casts — so fair is he —
A shadow on the throne?

Pray who has up to heaven come,
To heaven come, to heaven come,
Through all the circles seven come,
To fetch the Torah down?

'Tis Moses up to heaven come,
To heaven come, to heaven come,
Through all the circles seven come,
To fetch the Torah down.

SHAVUOT HYMN

BIKURIM LIRUSHALAYIM

March Solo
Ho-l'-him a – nu li – ru-sha-la-yim, li – ru-sha-la-yim, li – ru-sha-la-yim
Bi-ku-rim la – nu

Solo Girls: Boys:
Mi ho-leḥ i-ta-nu? Li – ru-sha-la-yim, li – ru-sha-la-yim, li – ru – sha – la-yim.
ku-la-nu.... ku-la-nu..

All:
Pa-nu de – reḥ la – nu! Bi-ku-rim nos-im a – nu! Li-

Boys: All:
-ru-sha-la-yim, li – ru-sha-la-yim, li – ru-sha-la ----- yim.

We're going to Jerusalem. Clear the way! We're going to Jerusalem, bringing Bikurim.

הוֹלְכִים אָנוּ לִירוּשָׁלַיִם,
בִּכּוּרִים לָנוּ לִירוּשָׁלַיִם.
מִי הוֹלֵךְ אִתָּנוּ לִירוּשָׁלַיִם?
כֻּלָנוּ, כֻּלָנוּ לִירוּשָׁלָיִם.
פַּנּוּ דֶרֶךְ לָנוּ!
בִּכּוּרִים נוֹשְׂאִים אָנוּ לִירוּשָׁלַיִם.

HEROES OF THE LAW

Moderato

When Mo-ses brought... the tab-lets down From Si-nai's mist..... en-cir-cled crown, He bore us from........ the heights he trod The

love of Is - - - rael and of God. And long the To - rah's words have made, The Jew-ish spi-rit..... un-a-fraid; The glo-rious pre-cepts that it taught Of fee-ble men have he-roes wrought.

Our priests and prophets, armed thereby,
In time of strife could do and die.
No threat of torture or disgrace
Could Israel's faith or soul efface.

Heroes are our eternal need —
Men like Akiba, strong in deed.
Would that such souls today might rise
To still our bitter, martyred cries!

SALENU

BIKURIM

סַלֵּינוּ עַל כְּתֵפֵינוּ,
רָאשֵׁינוּ עֲטוּרִים
מִקְצוֹת הָאָרֶץ בָּאנוּ,
הֵבֵאנוּ בִּכּוּרִים.

מִיהוּדָה, מִיהוּדָה, וּמִשׁוֹמְרוֹן,
מִן הָעֵמֶק, מִן הָעֵמֶק, וְהַגָּלִיל.

פַּנוּ דֶרֶךְ לָנוּ;
בִּכּוּרִים אִתָּנוּ.
הַךְ, הַךְ, הַךְ בַּתֹּף 2
וְחַלֵּל בָּחָלִיל!

TORAH LANU

D.C. al Fine

v'hik'do-sha. To-ra la — nu mo-ra-sha,... To-ra la — nu v'hik'do-sha.

D.C. al Fine

Oh praise the Lord. Holy is our heritage, the Torah. Sing unto Him and praise Him. The Lord was revealed at Mount Sinai.

Shi-ru lo, zam-ru lo,
Ro-nu lo, ho-du lo.
Ha-l'lu-yah....

B'ma-a-mad Har Si-nai,
Sham nig-la A-do-nai.
Ha-l'lu-yah....

הַלְלוּיָהּ, עִבְדוּ עַבְדֵי אֲדֹנָי.

תּוֹרָה לָנוּ מוֹרָשָׁה,
תּוֹרָה לָנוּ וְהִיא קְדוֹשָׁה.
הַלְלוּיָהּ...

שִׁירוּ לוֹ, זַמְרוּ לוֹ,
רֹנּוּ לוֹ, הוֹדוּ לוֹ.
הַלְלוּיָהּ...

בְּמַעֲמַד הַר סִינַי,
שָׁם נִגְלָה אֲדֹנָי.
הַלְלוּיָהּ...

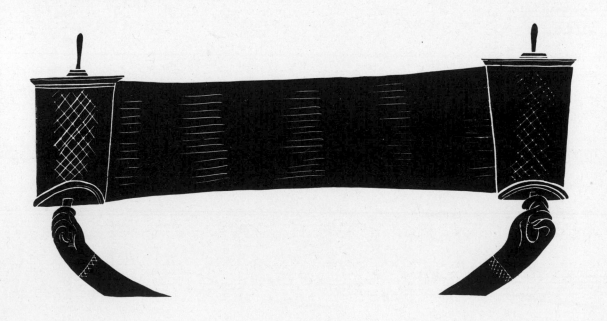

214

KUMU V'NA'ALE

215

Halleluyah! Praise the Lord in His sanctuary.
Come, let us go up to Zion, to the Lord our God.

הַלְלוּיָהּ, הַלְלוּיָהּ, הַלְלוּיָהּ, הַלְלוּ,
הַלְלוּיָהּ, הַלְלוּיָהּ, הַלְלוּ אֵל
בְּקָדְשׁוֹ.
קוּמוּ וְנַעֲלֶה צִיּוֹן,
אֶל ה' אֱלֹהֵינוּ.

URU AḤIM

D.C. AL FINE

ha-bi-ku-rim, Ha-bi-ku-rim,..... ha-bi-ku-rim, ha-bi-ku – rim ha-bi-ku-rim.....

Brothers arise and come to Zion's fair height!
Happy is he who in the land takes delight. We
bring to thee our Bikurim.

Hi-ney ma tov, ma tov, u-ma na-im,
She-vet a-ḥim, hoi she-vet gam ya-ḥad!

עוּרוּ אַחִים וְנַעֲלֶה הַר צִיּוֹן,
וְאָמְרוּ־נָא: אַשְׁרֵי הָעָם שֶׁכָּכָה לּוֹ.

מקהלה: מְלֹא הַטֶּנֶא, הַבִּכּוּרִים, (4)
הַבִּכּוּרִים, הַבִּכּוּרִים. (2)

הִנֵּה מַה טּוֹב, מַה טּוֹב, וּמַה נָּעִים,
שֶׁבֶת אַחִים, הוֹי שֶׁבֶת גַּם יַחַד!

BORUḤ ELOHENU

In march time

Bo-ruḥ E – lo-hey-nu she-bro – o-nu lih-vo-do
V'hiv – di – lo – nu....... min ha- – to-im

add 8va   loco

Blessed is the Lord who created us for His glory,
who distinguished us from the erring, who gave us
the Torah and everlasting life

בָּרוּךְ אֱלֹהֵינוּ שֶׁבְּרָאָנוּ לִכְבוֹדוֹ (3)
לִכְבוֹדוֹ.
עוֹד הַפַּעַם, עוֹד הַפַּעַם, לִכְבוֹדוֹ (3)

V'no-san lo-nu to-ras e-mes . . . .

Od ha-pa-am, to-ras e-mes . . . . .

וְהִבְדִּילָנוּ מִן הַתּוֹעִים . . .
עוֹד הַפַּעַם מִן הַתּוֹעִים . . .

וְנָתַן לָנוּ תּוֹרַת אֱמָת . . .
עוֹד הַפַּעַם תּוֹרַת אֱמָת . . .

V'ha-yey o-lom no-ta b'so-ḥe-nu . . . .

Od ha-pa-am, b'so-ḥe-nu . . . . .

וְחַיֵּי עוֹלָם נָטַע בְּתוֹכֵנוּ . . .
עוֹד הַפַּעַם בְּתוֹכֵנוּ . . .

TORAT EMET

Slowly

To - rat e - met . . . . na - tan l'a - mo El . . . .

Al yad n' - vi - o . . . . . ne - - man bey - - to . . . .

Lo ya-ḥa-lif...... ha – El v'-lo ya-mir...... da – to......

L'o-la-mim...... l'o – la-mim l'— – zu-la – to...........

The Lord has given the Torah of truth to His people through His faithful prophet. God will not change His law or alter it ever.

תּוֹרַת אֱמֶת נָתַן לְעַמּוֹ אֵל,
עַל יַד נְבִיאוֹ נֶאֱמַן בֵּיתוֹ.
לֹא יַחֲלִיף הָאֵל וְלֹא יָמִיר דָּתוֹ
לְעוֹלָמִים לְזוּלָתוֹ.

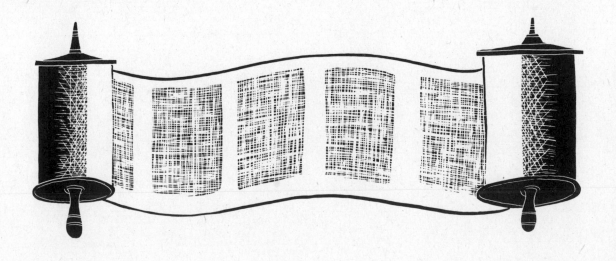

THE PILGRIMAGE

In March time

From the North of the land of Is-ra-el...... From the South and the West and the

East,...... The pil-grims come joy-ful-ly mar-ching To Je-ru-sa-lem ...... for the

add 8va........ loco

feast.------ Ah, ah, ah, ah............................... And

CHORUS

songs they sing and gifts they bring First.... fruits of ev'-ry

8va

sort; .... With mu - sic gay they come all day To the

Tem-ple, ... to the Tem-ple; To the gates of the Tem-ple court. ......

Now the Levites all wait for them to come,

And seeing them now, they begin:

"Oh this is the day which the Lord made,

Let us all be glad therein."

CHORUS

B'ney ha - k'far yotz - im ba - saḥ............

y' - vu - le - nu y' - vo - raḥ......... Ḥag, ḥag,... ḥag la - ke - rem,

ḥag la - p'ri Ḥag......... la - e - mek ha - iv - ri ha - iv - ri.

D.S. AL FINE

FINE

The villagers stream out to the fields. May our produce be blessed. The vines are crowned with clusters of grapes. How good to plant and plow, how good to drink the wine! Who created the dances for our light-stepping feet?

בְּנֵי הַכְּפָר יוֹצְאִים בַּסָּךְ,
יְבוּלֵנוּ יְבָרֵךְ.
חַג לַכֶּרֶם, חַג לַפְּרִי,
חַג לָעֵמֶק הָעִבְרִי.

עַל רֹאשֵׁנוּ אוֹר מָתוֹק
וּבְפִינוּ שִׁיר וּצְחוֹק.
הַגְּפָנִים כָּבְדוּ מְאֹד
בְּעִטּוּר הָאֶשְׁכּוֹלוֹת.

טוֹב לִזְרוֹעַ, טוֹב לַחֲרֹשׁ,
טוֹב לִשְׁתּוֹת אֶת הַתִּירוֹשׁ.
מִי יָצַר אֶת הַמְּחוֹלוֹת
לְרַגְלֵינוּ הַקַּלוֹת.

Al ro-she-nu or ma-tok
U-v'fi-nu shir u-tz'ḥok.

    Ha-g'fa-nim kav-du m'od
    B'i-tur ha-esh-ko-lot.

Tov liz-ro-a, tov la-ḥa-rosh,
Tov lish-tot et ha-ti-rosh.

    Mi ya-tzar et ha-m'ḥo-lot
    L'rag-ley-nu ha-ka-lot.

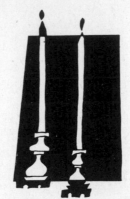

AL TIFG'I VI L'OZVEḤ

ENTREAT ME NOT TO LEAVE THEE

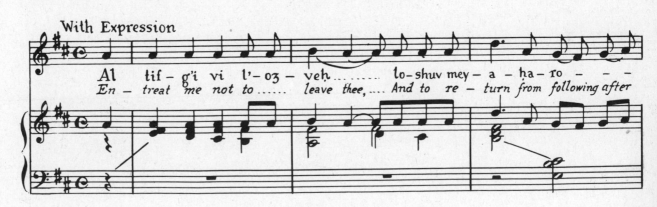

With Expression

Al tif-g'i vi l'-oz-veh...... lo-shuv mey-a-ha-ro---
En-treat me not to...... leave thee,.... And to re-turn from following after

yih,— Ki el a—sher tel-hi— e — leh,— u—va—a—sher — to-li-ni o-
thee; For whi-ther thou———go-est, I will go;——— And where thou lodg — est, I will

lin—— A — meh —— a — mi,—— ve-lo-ha-yih e-lo-
lodge;—— Thy peo-ple shall be my—— peo-ple, And thy — God ——

hoi.—— Ba-asher to — mu-si — o — mus,—— v' — shom e—ko—
my God; Where—— thou di-est—— will I die, And—— there will I be

Solo

ver.—— Ko ya-ase Ado-noi li—— v'-ho yo-sif,—— ki ha-
bu-ried; The Lord do so to me,—— and more al — so,—— If aught but

225

mo—ves yaf—rid beni u—ve—neh..... A—meh.... a—mi,.... ve—lo—
death....part thee and...... me...... Thy peo—ple.... shall be.... my peo—ple, And

—ha—yih e—lo—hoi........ A——meh........ a——mi...... ve—lo—
thy........ God, my...... God;..... Thy...... peo—ple shallbe...... my peo—ple and thy

ha—yih e—lo——hoi........ ve—lo—ha—yih e—lo—hoi.
God......... my...... God!...... and thy..... God....... my...... God.

עַמֵּךְ עַמִּי, וֵאלֹהַיִךְ אֱלֹהָי.
בַּאֲשֶׁר תָּמוּתִי אָמוּת, וְשָׁם אֶקָּבֵר.
כֹּה יַעֲשֶׂה יְיָ לִי וְכֹה יוֹסִיף,
כִּי הַמָּוֶת יַפְרִיד בֵּינִי וּבֵינֵךְ.

אַל תִּפְגְּעִי בִי לְעָזְבֵךְ, לָשׁוּב
מֵאַחֲרָיִךְ,
כִּי אֶל אֲשֶׁר תֵּלְכִי אֵלֵךְ, וּבַאֲשֶׁר
תָּלִינִי אָלִין.

226

Tishah B'av

ELI TZIYON

Moderato

E — li tzi — yon v — o — re — ho...... k-

-mo i — sho v — tzi — re — ho..... v — ḥiv — su — to...... ha-

-gu — ras sak...... al........ ba-al n — u — re — ho.

227

A song unto Zion who is like a woman in travail,
like a maiden mourning the husband of her youth

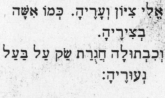

אֱלִי צִיּוֹן וְעָרֶיהָ. כְּמוֹ אִשָּׁה
בְּצִירֶיהָ.
וְכִבְתוּלָה חֲגֻרַת שַׂק עַל בַּעַל
נְעוּרֶיהָ:

A-ley ar-mon a-sher ni-tash b'ash-mas tzon
a-do-re-ho.

עֲלֵי אַרְמוֹן אֲשֶׁר נֻטַּשׁ בְּאַשְׁמַת
צֹאן עֲדָרֶיהָ.

V'al bi-as m'hor-fey El b'soh mik-dash ha-
do-re-ho:

וְעַל בִּיאַת מְחָרְפֵי אֵל בְּתוֹךְ מִקְדַּשׁ
חֲדָרֶיהָ:

A-ley go-lus m'shor-sey El, man-i-mey shir
z'mo-re-ho.

עֲלֵי גָלוּת מְשָׁרְתֵי אֵל. מַנְעִימֵי
שִׁיר. זְמָרֶיהָ.

V'al do-mom a-sher shu-pah, k'mo mey-mey
y'o-re-ho:

וְעַל דָּמָם אֲשֶׁר שֻׁפַּךְ. כְּמוֹ מֵימֵי
יְאוֹרֶיהָ:

AL NAHAROS BOVEL

BY THE WATERS OF BABYLON

228

shom yo-shav-nu Gam bo-hi-nu, b'-zoh-re-nu es Tzi-yon:...... b'-zoh-re-nu es Tzi-yon....
There we sat down and we wept, When we.... re — mem-bered thee... When we...... re — mem-bered thee....

עַל נַהֲרוֹת בָּבֶל, שָׁם יָשַׁבְנוּ
גַּם בָּכִינוּ, בְּזָכְרֵנוּ אֶת צִיּוֹן:

OVINU MALKENU

Our Father and King, be merciful unto us, for
we have no deeds to commend us.

Slowly with expression

O — vi-nu mal-ke — — — nu............... ho — ne—nu va — ne — —

nu .... o — vi-nu mal-ke—nu ho — — ne—nu va—ne—nu ki

-ne-nu va-ne—————nu.............. O—vi—nu mal-ke-nu ho-

-ne-nu va-ne-nu ki en bo-nu ma———sim.........................

אָבִינוּ מַלְכֵּנוּ, חָנֵנוּ וַעֲנֵנוּ,
כִּי אֵין בָּנוּ מַעֲשִׂים.
עֲשֵׂה עִמָּנוּ צְדָקָה וָחֶסֶד, וְהוֹשִׁיעֵנוּ.

SHIRU LANU

Not too slowly

Shi-ru lo-nu mi-shi-rey Tzi- yon! shi-ru lo-nu mi-shi-rey Tzi- yon! Eḥ no-

yon!........ Eh....... no - - shir al ad - mas ne - ḥor, al ad - mas ne - ḥor?...........

yon!........ Eh....... no - - shir........ al ...... ad - mas ne - ḥor?........

Shi-ru lo-nu mi-shi-rey Tzi - yon,................ shi-ru lo-nu mi-shi-rey Tzi - yon............

Eh............. no - - shir...... al ad - mas ne - ḥor, al ..... ad - mas ne - ḥor?

Sing us of the songs of Zion. How can we sing on strange soil?

שִׁירוּ לָנוּ מִשִּׁירֵי צִיּוֹן!
אֵיךְ נָשִׁיר עַל אַדְמַת נֵכָר?

233

ARTZA ALINU

WE ARE ASCENDING

March time

Oceans we're sailing, Mountains we're scaling Toward Israels holy

Ar-tza a-li-nu, ar-tza a-li-nu, ar-tza a-li - nu,..........
We are as-cend-ing, Our way we're wending To Is-rael's ancient land..........

With oct.

nu.......... K'-var ha-rash-nu v'-gam za-ra-nu, k'-var ha-rash-nu,
land.......... We've done our plow-ing Fi-nished our sow - ing; Worked with the har-row,

v'-gam za-ra-nu, A-val od lo ka-tzar-nu, A-val od lo ka-
En-ded our hoe-ing; But, tho we've sown with sad-ness, We've not yet reaped with

-tzar - nu, A - val od lo ka - tzar - nu, A - val od lo ka - tzar - nu.
glad - ness, We've not yet reaped with glad - ness We've not yet reaped with glad - ness.

אַרְצָה עָלִינוּ, אַרְצָה עָלִינוּ.
כְּבָר חָרַשְׁנוּ וְגַם זָרַעְנוּ,
אֲבָל עוֹד לֹא קָצַרְנוּ.

SAILING SONG

With a jolly swing

Sail-ing, we are sail-ing, our ship speeds a - cross the sea! Home-ward we are sail-ing to
Out on the ho - ri - zon Mount Car-mel will soon ap - pear, And in to the har-bor of

1. 2.

E - retz Yis-ra - el ho! Eastward, we are fac-ing, and swift-ly we are rac-ing, On the
Hai-fa we shall sail.

deep blue of the wa-ter, and the spar-kle of the foam...... We dare not tar-ry, For a

precious load we car-ry, Of..... brave young Ha—lu—tzim Who are seek-ing their new home, ho!

ANU OLIM

Joyous March

A-nu o-lim, o—lim ha-yom, a-nu o-lim o-

add 8va   loco

lim ha-yom, A-nu o-lim ha-yom, a-nu o-lim ha-yom, A-nu o-lim ha-yom.....

add 8va

yom......... La, la,.......

DAL %. AL FINE

A-nu bo-nim, bo-nim ha-yom.
A-nu o-lim ha-yom
A-nu bo-nim ha-yom.

אָנוּ עוֹלִים, עוֹלִים הַיּוֹם,
אָנוּ בּוֹנִים, בּוֹנִים הַיּוֹם.
אָנוּ עוֹלִים הַיּוֹם,
אָנוּ בּוֹנִים הַיּוֹם.

Today we go up to our land.
Today we build!
Today we go up to our land.

March

On-ward, on-ward bro-thers we're mar-ching For the land of Is-ra-el

fear-less, we strive. Let no doubt no dan-ger, E-ne-my nor stran-ger,

1.

2.

Keep us now from mar-ching on-ward, on-ward, on, on, on-ward on.

ASCENDING

To the moun-tain tops, to the moun-tain tops, The road shall not be barred For ex-iles re-turn-ing; From o'er..... the hill,..... us cal - ling still..... Is Zi - on, for her child-ren year - - ning. A- scend - ing, a - scend - ing To the moun-tain tops we're as-

242

-cend - - ing. A - scend - - ing, a - scend - - ing, to the

1. moun-tain tops we're a - scend - - ing A-

2. moun-tain tops we're a - scend-ing.

SONG OF THE HALUTZIM

March

Not as pil-grims, not as mour-ners Do we hail from Earth's four cor-ners To these hills and plains, hills and plains; For the storm that roars and ra-ges Brought to us the cry of a-ges, Bade us break our chains, break our chains..... From the

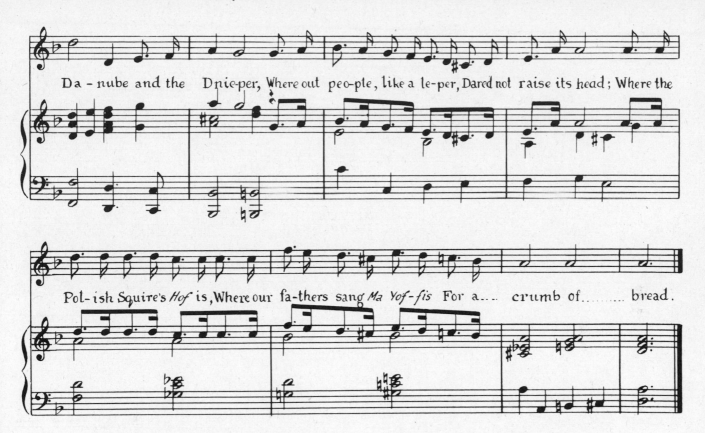

Da-nube and the Dnie-per, Where out peo-ple, like a le-per, Dared not raise its head; Where the

Pol-ish Squire's *Hof* is, Where our fa-thers sang *Ma Yof-fis* For a.... crumb of......... bread.

Thence we come with rod and rammer,
Come with wrench, and spade, and hammer
To build on stone and sand;
Till each waste and rock is witness
Of our will and skill and fitness
To re-shape our land.

Coming ages — we shall feed them
With the bread and fruit of freedom,
Not of shame and tears;
On the Carmel and the Tabor
Thus we sing and thus we labor —
We, the pioneers.

ZION, OUR MOTHER

wai-ting, we were looking to the goal;........... Thou wast al-ways cal-ling,

cal-ling us to haste; We were hop-ing and we heard thee in our soul.........

Other, men have found thee but a stony
    height,

It is we can bring the blessing to thy soil.

Only we, thy children, precious in thy sight,

We shall prove thee, we shall save thee by
    our toil.

Zion, our Mother, now thy sons depart,

We are coming while thou watchest there
    alone.

Heart amid the nations, beating with our
    heart,

We are ready, we are coming, we, thine own.

ALU, ALU

ARISE, ARISE

248

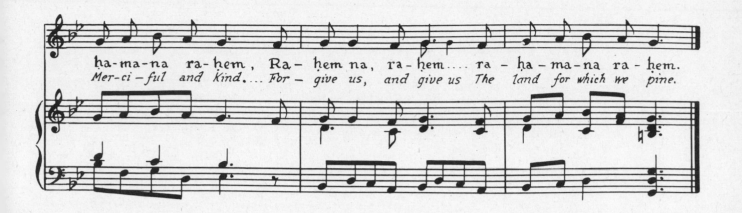

ha-ma-na ra-hem, Ra-hem na, ra-hem.... ra-ha-ma-na ra-hem.
Mer-ci-ful and kind.... For-give us, and give us The land for which we pine.

עֲלוּ, עֲלוּ לְאֶרֶץ אָבוֹת.

לְאַרְצֵנוּ עֲלוּ

בְּשִׁיר וּבִמְחוֹלוֹת.

תּוֹרַת אֱמֶת

הָאֵל נָתַן לָנוּ,

תּוֹרַת חַיִּים

הָאֵל נָטַע בָּנוּ.

יָהּ רִבּוֹן עוֹלָם (2),

רַחֵם (2), רַחֲמָנָא רַחֵם,

רַחֵם נָא, רַחֵם,

רַחֲמָנָא רַחֵם.

A SONG OF ZION

March

We are com-ing, com-ing, com-ing! Fling our ban-ner to the breeze! In

thou-sands we are com-ing from be-yond re-mo-test seas, We are com-ing af-ter cen-tu-ries of

sor-row and of toil...... To...... make our home in Is-ra-el and tread its ho-ly soil...... O

let the songs of glad-ness rise; let all the na-tions hear The an-thems of a might-y host of

Zi-on draw-ing near... A - cross the moun-tains, thru the vales, and o'er the o-cean's foam, Be-

hold the hosts of Is - ra - el are com-ing com-ing home!... A- com-ing com-ing home!

B'LEV YAM

Slowly

Ro - esh go-esh ha - yam, ... Ga - lav ḥot-rim la-

ḥof; .... No - s'im sh' - on daḥ - yam   Mi - - mer-ḥa-key en

sof. .... No - s'im sh' - on daḥ - - yam ...... Mi - mer-ḥa-key en   sof.

A ship is tossed about on the stormy sea, and on its decks exiles weep and pray: Bring us, O Lord, to Israel's land.

רוֹעֵשׁ גּוֹעֵשׁ הַיָּם,
גַּלָּיו חוֹתְרִים לַחוֹף;
נוֹשְׂאִים שְׁאוֹן דְּכָיִם
מִמֶּרְחַקֵּי אֵין סוֹף.

U-ven ga-ley ha-yam,
Sham o-ni-ya to-a.
U-va a-ḥim go-lim
Mi-mer-ḥa-key go-la.

וּבֵין גַּלֵּי הַיָּם,
שָׁם אֳנִיָּה תּוֹעָה.
וּבָהּ אַחִים גּוֹלִים
מִמֶּרְחַקֵּי גּוֹלָה.

252

V'ha-go-lim bo-ḥim,
Mit-pa-l'lim el El:
Ka-ḥe-nu av ra-ḥa-man,
L'e-retz Yis-ra-el!

וְהַגּוֹלִים בּוֹכִים,
מִתְפַּלְלִים אֶל אֵל:
קָחֵנוּ, אָב רַחֲמָן,
לְאֶרֶץ יִשְׂרָאֵל!

SHIR MA'APILIM

SONG OF THE MA'APILIM*

Ru-aḥ v'-to-ren rom va-a-fa-kim,
Waves roll and winds blow free, Tall stands the mast.

ḥo-fe-ḥa, sar ha-yam, ma r'-ho-kim. Ku-mu, ha-
Thy shores, o end-less Sea, How far, how vast! Come now,

sa-pa-nim, La-ma-shot, la-ma-shot, Ha-de-reh l'-fa-nim!
live-ly, men To your oar, to your oar, Our ship sails on a-gain,

Ha-su-fet ro-a-shot. Go-lu, go-lu ha-ga-lim, Go-lu gal ba-
Tho the storms blow and roar. Roll the waves, roll to the brim, Flood our hearts with

-lev. .... Hu-lu, hu-lu ma-pi-lim, Ha-na-mal ka-rev. ....
cheer .... Dance ye, dance ye ma-pi-lim Our har-bor's near. ....

*"Ma'apilim" is the Hebrew term applied to the post-war Jewish "illegal" immigrants who braved the British sea-blockade and the guns of the British boarding parties in order to reach Israel.

רוּחַ וְתֹרֶן רָם
וַאֲפָקִים.
חוֹפָיִךְ, שַׂר הַיָּם,
מָה רְחוֹקִים.

קוּמוּ, הַסַּפָּנִים,
לַמָּשׁוֹט, לַמָּשׁוֹט,
הַדֶּרֶךְ לְפָנִים!
הַסּוּפוֹת רוֹעֲשׁוֹת.

גְּלוּ, גְּלוּ, הַגַּלִּים,
גְּלוּ גַּל בַּלֵּב.
חוּלוּ, חוּלוּ, מַעְפִּילִים־
הַנָּמָל קָרֵב.

254

TO MY OWN SHORE

Hoi .... ma na – –im .... she-vet a–ḥim gam ya – ḥad. ....

Pick up speed

La, la, la ....

Get slower

slower

a tempo

To my own shore, homeland of yore,

Through foamy seas you brought me,

Vessel of grace; your masts I'll embrace,

Remem'bring the favors wrought me.

Restore, O Lord, our Zion, too long blighted!

How good indeed when brothers dwell
  united!

לְמוֹלַדְתִּי הֵבֵאת אוֹתִי

בְּיָם גַּלִים וָקֶצֶף,

אֶשַּׁק תְּרָנַיִךְ, אֳנִיָתִי,

וְלֹא אֶשְׁכָּחֵךְ לָנֶצַח.

פְּקֹד ד' פִּנַת צִיוֹן הַנִּדַחַת,

הוֹי מַה נָּעִים שֶׁבֶת אַחִים גַּם יָחַד.

ASHREY HA'ISH

Slowly

Ash - rey....... ha - ish yi-sa a-lu-mo - - tav....ash - -rey ha-ish Be-

-ma - a - le.......... ha-rey Tsi - - -yon..... ha - - rey Tzi-yon.

Mi................... yi - ten li e - ver........ ka - yo - na.......

Faster

...... A - u-fa sha-ma v'-esh-kon. So-lu, so - - lu Ha-m' si-la,...............

U - ru.... ha-g'-u - lim............... Ya-vo ya - vo - - u...... ba-sh'-a-

rit.   a tempo

rim........   De-reḥ pa- -nu la-g-u-lim........ De-reḥ.... hoi de-reḥ

Slow

pa-nu.... Hoi! pa-nu de-reḥ la-g'-u-lim........ .... la-g'-u- -lim....

אַשְׁרֵי הָאִישׁ יִשָּׂא אֲלוּמוֹתָיו
בְּמַעֲלֵה הָרֵי צִיּוֹן.
מִי יִתֶּן לִי אֵבֶר כַּיּוֹנָה
אָעוּפָה שָׁמָּה וְאֶשְׁכּוֹן.

סֹלּוּ, סֹלּוּ הַמְסִלָּה,
עוּרוּ הַגְּאוּלִים.
יָבוֹאוּ בַשְּׁעָרִים,
דֶּרֶךְ פַּנּוּ לַגְּאוּלִים.

Happy is the man who may bear his sheaves unto the hills of Zion. Make way for the redeemed who come streaming into the land! Oh, would that I had the wings of a dove to fly to Zion and nestle in its hills.

259

YAM LID

TO THE LAND OF ANCIENT PROMISE

Slowly - with feeling

Hob fer-ges-sen al-le lib-ste Hob..... fer- lost main ey- gn
I have for-got-ten all my loved ones, My house is fur- sa- ken and strange to

hoiz: Hob.....dem yam zih ob-ge-ge-bn: Trog mih
me; My fate I've en-trust-ed to the o-cean: Take me

yam tzum mu-ters shois............. Un du ma-riv vint ge-
home—ward, take me, sea............. To that shore, oh,..... bring me

trai— er, Traib main shif tzu..... ye-nem breg,......... Vos main
swift—ly, Blow thou... trust-y....... west-ern wind,......... To the

260

hartz.... mit od-ler fli — gel Zuht shoin lang tzu im a vu....
land...... of an-cient prom-ise Which my heart has....... yearned to find......

Breng miḥ nor a-hin b'sho-lom

Noḥ-dem flee ziḥ dir tzu-rik,

Gri-sn zol-stu a-le lib-ste

Un der-tzeyl zey fun main glik.

Un du ma-a-riv vint . . .

Bring me safely to that distant shore,

Thus back to your homeland you may fly,

Give my greetings to all my loved ones,

Tell them how much joy have I.

To that shore . . . . .

כ'האָב פֿאַרגעסען אַלע ליעבסטע
כ'האָב פֿאַרלאָזט מיין אייגען הויז:
כ'האָב דעם ים זיך אָבגענעבּען:
טראָן מיך ים צום מוטער'ס שויס.

און דו מאַעֶרב ווינד געטרייַער,
טרייַב מיין שיף צו יענעם בראָג,
וואָס מיין האַרץ מיט אָדלער פֿליעגעל
זוכט שוין לאַנג צו לאָנג צו איהם אַ וועג.

ברייַנג מיך נאָר אַהין בשלום
נאָכדעם פֿליה זיך דיר צוריק,
גריסען זאָלסטו אַלע ליעבסטע
און דערצעהל זיי פון מיין גליק.

און דו מאַעֶרב ווינד .....

AL TIRA AVDI YA'AKOV

Do not fear, my servant, Jacob. Arise, your path lies to the
east. The land shall belong to you and your descendants.

With spirit

Al ti - ra, av-di Yaa-kov, Hoi,ha-lam-ti ha-lom, Al ti - ra, av-di Yaa-kov,

Ma no-ra ha-mo-kom!.... Ni-tʒav lo ha-su-lam Im ma-la-ḥey sha-ma-yim Yor-

dim v'- o-lim ku-lam Im tʒ'-ḥo-rey ḥ'-na-fa- yim. Y'ya - - sher ko-ha-ha

THE WATCHMAN OF THE TOWER

I set my blocks, like walls, in rows, And then make tow-ers o - ver them; I build tall gates that o - pen, close, And in-side is Je - rus - a - lem. And I am the soldier,

bold and strong, Who watches, and who watch-es, O'er the walls so long; And

watch-es the tow-ers great and tall; And "All... is... well!" I proud-ly call.

If ever enemy should come,
No matter what his strength or might,
I'd blow my fife and beat my drum,
And I alone the foe would fight.

For I am the soldier, bold and strong,
Who watches, and who watches,
O'er the walls so long;
And watches the towers great and tall;
"The foe is beaten!" I would call.

And then when I had fought and won,
The enemy had run away —
And after all the fighting is done,
I'd stand and guard the walls all day.

For I am a soldier, bold and strong,
Who watches, and who watches,
O'er the walls so long,
And watches the towers great and tall
And "All's at peace!" then, I would call.

MOUNTAINS IN ISRAEL

No pa - la - ces in Is - ra - el, Few ci - ties rich and fine,..... But

moun-tains rise all 'round the skies, In a long and wa - - vy line....... But

moun-tains rise all 'round the skies In a long and wa - - vy line........

And there are valleys very deep,

With meadows painted bright,

Like carpets spread, embroidered red

And green and gold and white.

Like carpets spread, embroidered red

And green and gold and white.

And twenty camels on a string,

Go stalking up the track,

And leading all, a donkey small

With an Arab on its back.

And leading all, a donkey small

With an Arab on its back.

SIMḤU BIRUSHALAYIM

In a jolly manner

Sim-ḥu bi-ru-sha-la-yim, bi-Y'ru-sha-la—yim v'gi-lu, gi-lu, si-su, si-su,

i — ta ma-sos; Si-su i-ta ma-sos; Kol ha-mit-ab-lim a-le—ha,

Si-su i-ta ma-sos kol ha—mit-ab-lim a-le-ha, Si-su i-ta ma-sos.........

Kol ha-mit-ab-lim a — le-ha, si-su i-ta ma-sos..... kol ha-mit-ab-lim a-le—ha.

שִׂמְחוּ בִירוּשָׁלַיִם, בִּירוּשָׁלָיִם,
וְגִילוּ, שִׂישׂוּ אִתָּהּ מָשׂוֹשׂ;
שִׂישׂוּ אִתָּהּ מָשׂוֹשׂ
כָּל הַמִּתְאַבְּלִים עָלֶיהָ.

HEN LO ḤARASHTI

I DID NO PLOWING

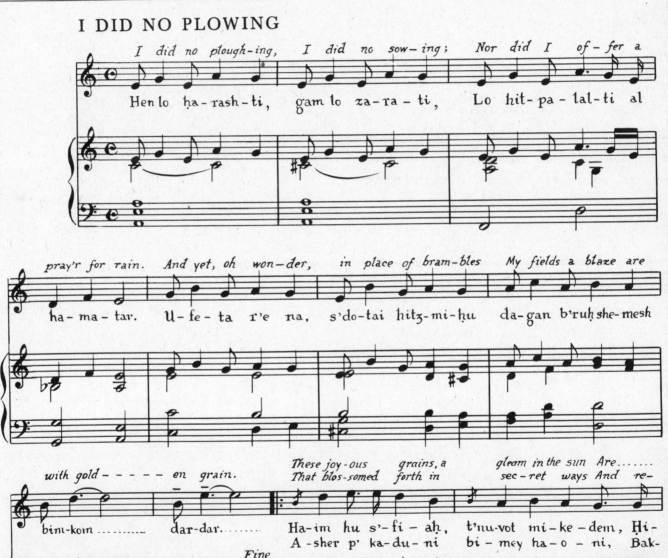

I did no plough-ing, I did no sow-ing; Nor did I of-fer a
Hen lo ḥa-rash-ti, gam lo za-ra-ti, Lo hit-pa-lal-ti al

pray'r for rain. And yet, oh won-der, in place of bram-bles My fields a blaze are
ha-ma-tar. U-fe-ta r'e na, s'do-tai hitz-mi-ḥu da-gan b'ruḥ she-mesh

with gold - - - - - en grain.
bim-kom . . . . dar-dar . . . . . .

Fine

These joy-ous grains, a gleam in the sun Are . . . .
That blos-somed forth in sec-ret ways And re-
Ha-im hu s'-fi-aḥ, t'nu-vot mi-ke-dem, Hi-
A-sher p' ka-du-ni bi-mey ha-o-ni, Bak-

268

they a har—vest from
mem—bered me in my

1. an—cient seed.
2. hour of need.....

tey hed—va hem, k'tzu—rim me—az?
u, a—lu vi b'—

o——rah raz.....

D.C. al Fine

D. C al Fine

הֵן לֹא חָרַשְׁתִּי, גַּם לֹא זָרַעְתִּי,
לֹא הִתְפַּלַּלְתִּי עַל הַמָּטָר.
וּפֶתַע רְאֵה נָא, שְׂדוֹתַי הִצְמִיחוּ דָגָן,
בָּרוּךְ־שֶׁמֶשׁ בִּמְקוֹם דַּרְדָּר.

הַאִם הוּא סְפִיחַ תְּנוּבוֹת מְקֶּדֶם,
חִטֵּי חָדְנָה הֵם, קְצוּרִים מֵאָז,
אֲשֶׁר פְּקָדוּנִי בִּימֵי הָעֹנִי,
בָּקְעוּ, עָלוּ בִי, בְּאֹרַח רָז?

ZEMER LAḤ

With spirit

Ze—mer, ze—mer laḥ, ze—mer, ze—mer laḥ,
Ha ma ḥot so vev, ze—mer laḥ do—vev

1. Ze—mer laḥ, m'—ho—ra—ti, m'—ho—ra—ti.....
2. —ti, m'—ho—ra—ti..... Ha—r'—ra—yiḥ
ze—mer laḥ m'—ho—ra

269

hey-ma yis-ma-ḥu Et m'-ḥol ha-ho-ra yis - ar,.......... E – lef p'ra-ḥim l'-

fe-ta yif-ra-ḥu Y-ḥa-su et p'ney ha-mid - bar.......... bar.

A song to you, my fatherland. The hills rejoice as we sing and dance the hora. A thousand flowers shall suddenly blossom upon the face of the wilderness.

זֶמֶר זָמַר לָךְ, זֶמֶר זָמַר לָךְ,
זָמַר לָךְ, מְכוֹרָתִי,
הַמָּחוֹל סוֹבֵב, זָמַר לָךְ דּוֹבֵב,
זָמַר לָךְ, מְכוֹרָתִי.

הֲרָרַיִךְ הֵמָה יִשְׂמָחוּ,
עֵת מְחוֹל הַהוֹרָה יִסְעָר,
אֶלֶף פְּרָחִים לְפֶתַע יִפְרָחוּ,
יְכַסּוּ אֶת פְּנֵי הַמִּדְבָּר.

270

ADAMA

271

At i-mey-nu .. a-da-ma, At ad-mat, ad — mat kol hai.

Ah,............ Ah,............ A-da-ma,..... a-da-ma.

Ah,............ Ah,............ A-da-ma,..... a-da-ma

Dal $\mathcal{S}$ la Coda

CODA

A-da-ma,.... a-da-ma,.. A-da-ma,.... a-da-ma....

O land, you are our mother. In the low places and in the high, in the rain and in the sun, in hunger and in thirst, you are our comfort, the source of all life.

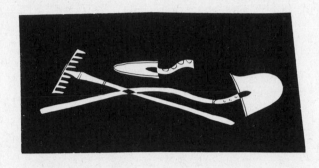

אָ, אֲדָמָה, אֲדָמָה,
בַּשְׁפֵלָה וּבָרָמָה, אָ!
בְּמָטָר וּבַחַמָּה, אָ!
אַתְּ אִמֵּנוּ, אֲדָמָה,
אַתְּ אַדְמַת כָּל חָי,
אָ, אֲדָמָה, אֲדָמָה.

בְּרָעָב וּבַצָּמָא, אָ!
בָּךְ מְקוֹר הַנֶּחָמָה, אָ!
אַתְּ אִמֵּנוּ אֲדָמָה,
אַתְּ אַדְמַת, אַדְמַת כָּל חָי,
אָ, אֲדָמָה, אֲדָמָה.

NATATI ETZ

I PLANTED A TREE

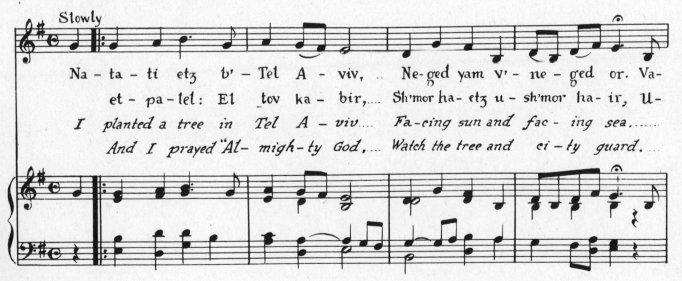

Slowly

Na - ta - ti etz b'- Tel A - viv, ... Ne - ged yam v'- ne - ged or. Va-
et - pa - lel: El tov ka - bir, ... Sh'mor ha - etz u - sh'mor ha - ir, U-
I planted a tree in Tel A - viv ... Fa - cing sun and fac - ing sea ......
And I prayed "Al - migh - ty God, Watch the tree and ci - ty guard.

a-va-reḥ o - to ley-mor: A - sey a - naf, p'- ros tzel sa-viv! Vash'morna et a - mal ha-am... Me-ru-aḥ ra, mi-sa-ar... yam. Na-

And I blessed the tree to be,........ "Put forth branch and sha-dy...... leaf"
And save, pray, our peo-ple's toil From blight-ing winds, and tem-pests...foil." I....

ta - ti etz b'- Tel A - viv,........ Ne - ged yam v'- ne - ged or.....
planted a tree in Tel A - viv,........ Fa - cing sun and fa - cing sea.....

וָאֶתְפַּלֵּל: אֵל טוֹב כַּבִּיר,
שְׁמֹר הָעֵץ וּשְׁמֹר הָעִיר,
וּשְׁמֹר נָא אֶת עֲמַל-הָעָם
מֵרוּחַ רַע, מִסַּעֲרַ-יָם.

נָטַעְתִּי עֵץ בְּתֵל אָבִיב,
נֶגֶד יָם וְנֶגֶד אוֹר.
וָאֲבָרֵךְ אוֹתוֹ לֵאמֹר:
עֲשֵׂה עָנָף, פְּרֹשׂ צֵל סָבִיב!

Y'RUSHALAYIM

Slowly, with feeling

Me-al pis-gat...... Har ha-Tzo-fim Esh - tah-ve lah a - pa-yim,...... Me-al pis-gat...... Har ha-Tzo-fim, Sha - lom lah Y'-ru-sha- la-yim,....... Mey-a do-rot ha - lam-ti a-la-yih, Liz - kot lir-ot b' - or pa-na-yih.....Y'-

ru - sha-la-yim, Y' - ru - sha-la-yim, ha - i-ri pa-na-yich liv - neh!....... Y'-

ru - sha-la yim, Y' - ru - sha-la-yim! Me - hor - vo-ta-yih ev - neh!..........

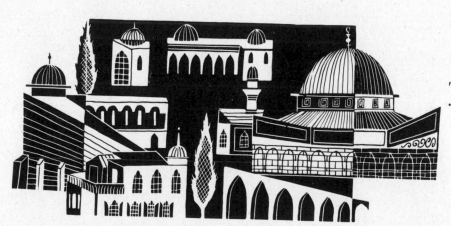

מֵעַל פִּסְגַּת הַר הַצּוֹפִים,
אֶשְׁתַּחֲוֶה לָךְ אַפַּיִם,
מֵעַל פִּסְגַּת הַר הַצּוֹפִים,
שָׁלוֹם לָךְ, יְרוּשָׁלָיִם.
מֵאָה דוֹרוֹת חָלַמְתִּי עָלַיִךְ,
לִזְכּוֹת לִרְאוֹת בְּאוֹר פָּנָיִךְ.

יְרוּשָׁלַיִם, יְרוּשָׁלַיִם!
הָאִירִי פָּנַיִךְ לִבְנֵךְ!
יְרוּשָׁלַיִם, יְרוּשָׁלַיִם!
מֵחָרְבוֹתַיִךְ אֶבְנֵךְ!

From the top of Mount Scopus I greet you, Jerusalem. For hundreds of years have I dreamt of you, I and thousands of exiles the world over. I shall reclaim you from your desolation, O Jerusalem.

Slowly, with feeling

Mi yit-ne-ni...... of...... Tzi - por ka-naf k'ta-na......... ha!

Bin-du-dey en sof.........naf — shi ma mit-a — na....... ha!

ha!......... Bin-du – dey en sof..... Naf – –shi ma mit-a – na...........

Mi yit-ne-ni of	מִי יִתְּנֵנִי עוֹף,	מִי יִתְּנֵנִי עוֹף
Tzi-por ka-naf k'ta-na.	צִפּוֹר־כָּנָף קְטַנָּה.	צִפּוֹר־כָּנָף קְטַנָּה . . . הָהּ!
A-sher ba-ken ha-tov	אֲשֶׁר בַּקֵּן הַטּוֹב	בִּנְדוּדֵי אֵין סוֹף
Ta-nu-aḥ sha-a-na-na.	תָּנוּחַ שַׁאֲנַנָּה.	נַפְשִׁי מַה מִּתְעַנָּה.
A-ha! K'of no-ded	אֲהָהּ! כְּעוֹף נוֹדֵד	
A-nud a-ni gam ken,	אָנוּד אֲנִי גַם כֵּן,	*Oh, that I were a bird, that I might rest secure*
Aḥ et i-af m'od	אַךְ עֵת אִיעַף מְאֹד	*in my nest. For although I wander about like a*
La-nu-aḥ en li ken.	לָנוּחַ אֵין לִי קֵן.	*bird, I have no nest when I grow weary.*

277

AD OR HABOKER

TILL BREAK OF MORNING

LONGING FOR JERUSALEM

glo - ry passed a - way............... Had
ser - pent dwells a - lone............... Could I but kiss thy

dust So would I fain ex - pire,..........As sweet as ho - ney

then................. My long - ing...... my .... de - sire.................

KAHA KAH

yom shi-ri li lai-la,... Ar-tzi ha-rim ha-rim v'-

gai .... la, ... Ar-tzi ha-rim ha-rim v'-

gai - la. .... Hoi shi-ri li yom shi-ri li lai-la, ...

Ar-tzi ha-rim ha-rim v'-gai ...... la, ...

Shi-ri li, shi-ri li od v'od,......... E - ras-tih li

bid - ma - ot.......................... bid - ma - ot..........

So were you then, and so today. O Bashan, Gilead,
Kinneret, Mediterranean; O hills and valleys of Zion,
I would not have you otherwise. I sing of you by
day, by night. In joy and in sorrow, I am yours
forever.

Ka-ḥa kaḥ v'lo a-ḥe-ret, im ha-t'ḥe-let
  ha-maz-he-ret,
Im mer-ḥav ho-lot nir-dam, al
  ha-ne-fesh al ha-a-dam.

  Hoi, shi-ri li yom . . . . .

כָּכָה כָּךְ וְלֹא אַחֶרֶת, יָם תִּיכוֹן
וְיָם כִּנֶּרֶת,
גַּם בָּשָׁן וְגַם גִּלְעָד, מִנִּי אָז וַעֲדֵי
עַד.

הוֹי, שִׁירִי לִי יוֹם, שִׁירִי לִי
לַיְלָה,
אַרְצִי הָרִים וְנַי לָהּ,
שִׁירִי לִי, שִׁירִי לִי עוֹד וְעוֹד,
אַרְשֹׁתִיךְ לִי בִּדְמָעוֹת.

כָּכָה כָּךְ וְלֹא אַחֶרֶת, עִם הַתְּכֵלֶת
הַמַּזְהֶרֶת,
עִם מֶרְחַב חוֹלוֹת נִרְדָּם, עַל
הַנֶּפֶשׁ עַל הָאָדָם.

הוֹי, שִׁירִי לִי יוֹם
. . . . .

A-na-nim..... ka-lim ya-nu..... Ru-aḥ kal.... ro-hesh.....

B'ni a-vi-ha mi-Ya-gur... Bish-lom-ha do - - - resh...........

B'ni a-vi-ha mi-Ya-gur......... Bish-lomha do - resh.......... di. ....

My son, your father sends you greetings from Yagur, where he fights for freedom. You too, shall be a hero. Sleep, my child and grow strong.

עֲנָנִים קַלִּים יָנוּעוּ,
רוּחַ קַל רוֹחֵשׁ,
בְּנִי, אָבִיךָ מִיָּגוּר
בִּשְׁלוֹמְךָ דּוֹרֵשׁ.

B'so-rot me-vi ha-ru-aḥ
Mi-maḥ-ne ha-hes-ger.
Sham o-med a-ta a-vi-ha
Al k'vod a-mo sho-mer.

בְּשׂוֹרוֹת מֵבִיא הָרוּחַ
מִמַּחֲנֵה הַהָסְגֵּר,
שָׁם עוֹמֵד עַתָּה אָבִיךְ
עַל כְּבוֹד עַמּוֹ שׁוֹמֵר.

285

Lo kor-ban a-ha-ron a-vi-ha
B'mil-he-met d'ror,
Al tid-ag, yal-di, hin-ha
Ben l'av gi-bor.

B'ni, ti-ye gi-bor gam a-ta,
Nu-ma, mah-ma-di.
Ve-e-zor et ko-ho-te-ha
Le-a-tid, yal-di.

לֹא קָרְבָּן אַחֲרוֹן אָבִיךְ
בְּמִלְחֶמֶת דְּרוֹר,
אַל תִּדְאַג, יַלְדִּי, הִנְּךָ
בֶּן לְאָב גִּבּוֹר.

בְּנִי, תִּהְיֶה גִּבּוֹר גַּם אַתָּה,
נוּמָה, מַחֲמַדִּי.
וְאֶזּוֹר אֶת כְּחוֹתֶיךָ
לֶעָתִיד, יַלְדִּי.

YISHTABER V'YITROMEM

WE ARE LIKE A MIGHTY WALL

With spirit

Yish - ta - ber v' - yit - ro - mem   ke - tzef ha-ga-lim b' - ra-ash...
Let   the waves break on our shore,   Foa - my waves in an-ger pound-ing;

Yit ga - ber v' - yit - ko - mem   za - am mish-ba-rim b' - ga-ash;   Hit-la - k' - du u-
Let the break-ers crash and roar,   E - choes on the shore re - sound-ing;   Join in the dance in

va — ma — gal v'— rik-du b'— esh va-ke-tzef So— v'— vu u-
cir-cle and swirl, Dance with spir-it till the mor-row; Round and round, and

-va-gal-gal Shi-h'-hu ya—gon va-e-tzev A—nu po ho—mat ma—gen,
in the whirl Cast a-way your grief and sor-row. We are like a migh-ty wall,

ha-ga-lim na—tzo-ra, la—nu ru-ah t'—na—gen... ho-ra, ho-ra,
Back the wild waves fling-ing; All the winds shall back our call..... Ho-ra, Ho-ra,

ho—ra.... la—nu ru-ah t'—na—gen,... ho-ra ho-ra ho-ra!
sing-ing!.... All the winds shall back our call.... Ho-ra, Ho-ra, sing-ing!

Yit-ba-zek v'yiz-da-her
No-ga ha-ba-rak b'ra-am;
Yit-ḥa-zek v'yis-ta-er
Sa-ar ha-su-fa b'za-am.

Me-e-ne-nu ha-ba-rak,
Mi-li-be-nu ze ha-na-ham;
Hit-ḥaz-ku v'nit-ḥa-zak
V'nir-ko-da zot ha-pa-am. —

CHORUS
    A-nu po ḥo-mat ma-gen. . . .

Let the lightning streak the sky,
While the thunder peals its chorus;
Let the wild winds storm and sigh,
While the tempest rages o'er us;

From our hearts, the thundering deep,
From our eyes, the lightning glancing;
Ready and brave, vigil we keep
As we join once more in dancing. —

CHORUS:
    We are like a mighty wall, ...

יִשְׁתַּבֵּר וְיִתְרוֹמֵם
קֶצֶף הַגַּלִּים בְּרַעַשׁ;
יִתְגַּבֵּר וְיִתְקוֹמֵם
זַעַם מִשְׁבָּרִים בְּנַעַשׁ;

הִתְלַכְּדוּ – וּבַמַּעְגָּל,
וְרִקְדוּ בְּאֵשׁ וָקֶצֶב;
סוֹבְבוּ וּבַגַּלְגַּל
שִׁכְחוּ יָגוֹן וָעֶצֶב.

מקהלה   אָנוּ פֹּה חוֹמַת מָגֵן,
הַגַּלִּים נֶעֱצוֹרָה;
לָנוּ רוּחַ תְּנַגֵּן –
הוֹרָה, הוֹרָה, הוֹרָה!

יִתְבַּזֵּק וְיִזְדַּהֵר
נֹגַהּ הַבָּרָק בְּרַעַם;
יִתְחַזֵּק וְיִשְׂתָּעֵר
סַעַר הַסּוּפָה בְּזַעַם;

מֵעֵינֵינוּ הַבָּרָק,
מִלִּבֵּנוּ זֶה הַנַּהַם;
הִתְחַזְּקוּ וְנִתְחַזַּק
וְנִרְקוֹדָה זֹאת הַפַּעַם –

מקהלה   אָנוּ פֹּה חוֹמַת מָגֵן. . . .

288

NIKRA'IM AḤIM BALAYIL

IN THE NIGHT A CALL FOR BROTHERS

March, very sustained

Nik-ra - im a - him ba - la - yil, A - lu-mey go-
In the night a call for bro - thers, Un-be-known their

ral va - shem, Nik-ra - im pit-om la - ha - yil Ha-tzo-ed u-
name or plight. Sud-den called to arms, like o - thers Mar-ching forth un-

mit-a - lem. Ya-a-mod p'lo-ni la-ma-vet, Ya-a-mod p'lo-ni la - shod!
to the night. Some shall die be - fore the mor-row, Some shall live thru fire and flames!

B'-mis-ge-ret ha-a-tza-vet Ti-pa-kad-na ha-n'sa-shot Mi-kol go-
In this vale of grief and sor - row Sounds the ros-ter of their names. From the rol-

-ren bis-dot e-ver, Mi-kol o— — — hel v'-su-ka,.... Mitz-tar-fim, yor-
-ling fields and mea-dows, From each tent.......... and shel-tered booth, Men who'll know the

dey el ke-ver la-shu-ra.... ha-a-'ru-ka.... Ko-ha-
graves deep sha-dows Join the ranks of mar-tyred youth. Tremb-ling

vim .... to—him .... b'— —ra — — ad,..........
stars .... for—sake .... their cal — — -ling,

za-ha-ru-rim .... ba—yam ka—vim,.......... He— resh,
O'er the dark sea.......... no lights burn,.......... Si — lent!

ah ka — ved hu tza — ad Ha-hol-him, v'— lo sha — vim.
Hear the foot-steps fal — ling Of the men who'll ne'er re-turn.

נִקְרָאִים אַחִים בַּלַּיִל,
עֲלוּמֵי גוֹרָל וָשֵׁם.
נִקְרָאִים פִּתְאֹם לַחַיִל
הַצּוֹעֵד וּמִתְעַלֵּם.

מִכָּל גֹּרֶן בִּשְׂדוֹת עָבַר,
מִכָּל אֹהֶל וְסֻכָּה,
מִצְטָרְפִים יוֹרְדֵי אֶל קֶבֶר
לַשּׁוּרָה הָאֲרֻכָּה.

יַעֲמֹד פְּלוֹנִי לַמָּוֶת,
יַעֲמֹד פְּלוֹנִי לַשּׁוֹד!
בְּמִסְגֶּרֶת הָעַצֶּבֶת
תִּפָּקַדְנָה הַנְּפָשׁוֹת.

כּוֹכָבִים תּוֹהִים בְּרַעַד,
זַהֲרוּרִים בַּיָּם כָּבִים.
חֶרֶשׁ, אַךְ כָּבֵד הוּא צָעַד
הַהוֹלְכִים וְלֹא שָׁבִים.

SHIR LANEGEV

With feeling

At a-da-ma b'-lev mid-bar. L'-lo tzel etz, l'-lo ma-tar. tar.

(Like a flute from afar)

291

El mer-ḥa - veh nad-ri - ma. A-mar-nu ki na-si- ma, Pa - ne - nu ha-neg – ba.   ba.

B'ad ma-teḥ me-kor ḥa-yim,
T'hi ze-a-te-nu l'me-tar r'vi-vim;

CHORUS:
    El mer-ḥa-veḥ . . .

Ka-a-fi-kim ba-ne-gev
Yish-te yir-ve kol re-gev.

CHORUS:
    El mer-ḥa-veḥ . . .

בְּאַדְמָתֵךְ מְקוֹר חַיִּים,
תְּהִי זֵעָתֵנוּ לִמְטַר רְבִיבִים:

מקהלה:

כָּאֲפִיקִים בַּנֶּגֶב
יִשְׁתֶּה יִרְוֶה כָּל רָגֶב.

מקהלה:

אַתְּ אֲדָמָה בְּלֵב מִדְבָּר,
לְלֹא צֵל עֵץ, לְלֹא מַטָּע.

מקהלה: אֶל מֶרְחָבֵךְ נַדְרִימָה,
אָמַרְנוּ כִּי נָשִׁימָה
פָּנֵינוּ הַנֶּגְבָּה!

A source of life is your dear sod,
May our sweat refresh each clod;

Let the Negev's thirst be quenched
Its parched soil with dew be drenched.

Moderato

The-let sha-ma-yim mo-she-het ba - rom ... v'-
la-yih ki-ne-ret la-shut b'—li sof ...

sod en ha-he-ker mo-sheh e—ley t'hom ... kol ya-
bah hish-ta-kef v'-le-hov v—le—hov ... hish-ta-

gon v'-hol o-sher v'-gil m'-ley pa-hat ... Ah ... Al ga-
peh b'-ri-na u-b'-be-hi gam ya-had ...

Ah

at pe-le

Ta-ḥat sha-ma-yiḥ liḥ-yot v'-la-mut... At pe-le kol pe-le a-le a-da-mot........ Ki-

ne-ret............. Ki-ne-ret............ At pe - - - - le.........

The blue of the sky is a magnet,

Yet thy depths are a bottomless dragnet;

O Kinneret, 'tis awesome yet full of peace,

To float on thy billowing waves without cease.

To revel in thee, to love and to cherish;

May this mixture of sadness and joy never perish.

Kinneret, Kinneret, spacious in size,

Almighty God dwells in your waves;

To live and to die under your skies,

O wonder of wonders, is what my heart craves.

Kinneret, Kinneret.

תְּכֵלֶת שָׁמַיִם מוֹשֶׁכֶת בָּרוֹם

וְסוֹד אֵין־הַחֵקֶר מוֹשֵׁךְ אֱלֵי תְהוֹם.

כָּל יָגוֹן וְכָל אֹשֶׁר וְגִיל מָלֵא פַחַד,

עַל גַּלַּיִךְ, כִּנֶּרֶת, לָשׁוּט בְּלִי סוֹף.

בָּךְ הִשְׁתַּקֵּף וְלֶאֱהֹב, וְלֶאֱהֹב,

הִשְׁתַּפֵּךְ בְּרִנָּה וּבִבְכִי גַּם יַחַד.

כִּנֶּרֶת, כִּנֶּרֶת, אַתְּ פֶּלֶא כָּל פֶּלֶא,

אֱלֹהַּ הַנֵּצַח בָּךְ חַי בַּתְּהוֹמוֹת,

תַּחַת שָׁמַיִךְ לִחְיוֹת וְלָמוּת.

אַתְּ פֶּלֶא כָּל פֶּלֶא עֲלֵי אֲדָמוֹת,

כִּנֶּרֶת, כִּנֶּרֶת.

ON HILL, IN VALE

March

On hill, in vale, let each his fel-low hail, Hur-rah, hur-rah, re-

sound — ing. We shout, we sing, we let our voi-ces ring,....... New

life, new hope, a-bound-ing. Op-pres-sion is dead, the

black cloud is fled, Our joy fills all cre - a - tion; Our faith is sup-reme, ful-

filled is our dream, Our dream of land and na - tion. Op- na - tion.

SONG OF THE WATCHMAN

Moderately fast

Glee reigns in Ga-li-lee, The Ga-lil re - joic - es;

The day and ...... the   night... round...   Lift   up   your   voic - es.   *FINE*

Thru nights witch - ing... dark - - - ness, A ... flute soft - ly sound - ing, The
Sing ho,.....my.... Ga - li - lee, Oh,.... sing on my heart - strings;...

watch - man of Ga - li - lee, His watch - song re - sound - ing.   *D.C.*
With gun and my no - ble steed, I .... fear not.... what fate brings.

Who am I, what have I,
Without thee, my Galil?
Glorious Galilee;
I love thee, my Galil.

KUMA EḤA

COME, O BROTHERS

min.... ha-krah, B........ her-mesh u – va – – a – nah.... Ku – ma e – ha,
men of the plow,... All in ac-cord then to one God will bow..... come, O Bro-thers

sov........ va – sov,.... Al.......... ta – nu – ha.... sho – – va shov.......
round..... and round, Rest........ to – mor – row,.... in Song now re – sound;....

En...... kan rosh, v' – en..... kan sof,.... Yad... el yad.... al ta – a – zov.
None here is first and none here is last,..... Hands on shoul-ders hold firm and fast,

Yom... sha-ka v' – yom....... yiz-rah, A – nu ne-fen ah......... el ah,
This day will set a new day will dawn, Bro-ther to bro-ther in love will be drawn;

Min ha-k'far u min ha-k'rah, B' her-mesh u va a-nah.
Men of the pen and men of the plow, All in ac-cord Then to one God will bow.

יוֹם שָׁקַע וְיוֹם יִזְרַח,   קוּמָה, אָחָא, סֹב וְסֹב,

אָנוּ נֵפֶן אָח אֶל אָח,   אַל תְּנוּחָה, שׁוּבָה שׁוּב.

מִן הַכְּפָר וּמִן הַכְּרָךְ   אֵין כָּאן רֹאשׁ וְאֵין כָּאן סוֹף,

בְּחֶרְמֵשׁ וּבָאֵת.   יָד אֶל יָד, אַל תַּעֲזֹב.

TEḤEZAKNA

OH STRENGTHEN

Te-he-zak-na y'-de kol a-he-nu ha-m'ho-n'nim,... Af-rot ar-tze-nu ba-a-
Oh..... streng-then the hands of our com-rades, Re-buil-ding the Land of our Fa-thers with the

sher hem... sham Al yi-pol... ru-ha-hem a-li-zim mit-ro-n'-nim,
sweat of their brow......... Toil-ing cou-ra-geous in the dream of the a-ges

Bo - u sh'hem e - had l' - ez - - rat ha - am. Al yi - pol........ ru - ḥa - ḥem a -
Shoul-der to shoul-der for Is - ra - el now........ Toil-ing cou - ra - - geous in the

li - zim mit - ro - n' - nim, Bo - u sh'hem e - had l' - ez - rat ha - am.
dream of the a - - ges Shoul-der to shoul-der for Is - - ra - el now.

Mi vaz l'yom k'ta-not, ha-buz la-mit-lo-tz'tzim.

Mal-tu et am-ḥem v'i-tim a-su —

Ad nish-ma me-ra-shey he-ha-rim mit-po-tz'tzim,

Ko-lot A-do-nai ha-ko-r'im: A-lu.

Behold with the tears of our past shall be mingled

The sweat of your brow and the blood of your heart

Poured without measure we'll guard as our treasure

Set in the shrine of the nation apart.

תֶּחֱזַקְנָה יְדֵי כָּל אַחֵינוּ הַמְחוֹנְנִים,
עַפְרוֹת אַרְצֵנוּ בַּאֲשֶׁר הֵם שָׁם;
אַל יִפֹּל רוּחֲכֶם, עֲלִיזִים,
מִתְרוֹנְנִים,
בֹּאוּ שְׁכֶם אֶחָד לְעֶזְרַת הָעָם!

מִי בָז לְיוֹם קְטַנּוֹת, הַבּוּז
לַמִּתְלוֹצְצִים.
מַלְטוּ אֶת עַמְּכֶם וְאִתִּים עֲשׂוּ —
עַד נִשְׁמַע מֵרָאשֵׁי הֶהָרִים
מִתְפּוֹצְצִים,
קוֹלוֹת אֲדֹנָי הַקּוֹרְאִים: עֲלוּ.

NIGUN BIALIK

La la la la   etc.

MIDAN AD B'ER SHEVA

306

*From Dan to Beersheba, from Gilead to the sea,
every field and hill has been redeemed with the blood
of Jews. But never was purer blood shed than that
of the tillers of Tel Ḥai.*

מִדָּן עַד בְּאֵר שֶׁבַע,
מִגִּלְעָד לַיָּם,
אֵין אַף שַׁעַל אַדְמָתֵנוּ –
לֹא כֻפַּר בַּדָּם.
דָּם עִבְרִי רָווּי לְשֶׁבַע
נִיר, הַר וָגַי,
אַךְ מִדֹּר לְדֹר
לֹא נִשְׁפַּךְ דָּם טָהוֹר
מִדַּם חוֹרְשֵׁי תֵּל-חָי.

SOV'VUNI

DANCE AROUND ME

So - v'-vu - ni   la - hat, esh bo - e - ret,   Ra - k'-du li
Dance a -round me,   flames and rag-ing fire....   I shall join in

shir ya-hid,......   Ze ha-ze - mer.,   ze v'-en a-her od
dance ere long.........   Hear my sing-ing,   hear my heart's de-sire;......

Moonlight, moonlight, moonlight
in our homeland,

Moonlight kindles spirits fast.

All our life is like a flaming fire-
brand

For the future and the past.

Dance, dance, dance the *hora*,

Dance the *hora* without end.

Naught can stop us now, my
friend —

With the night spread out about us

And our land stretched out beyond
us.

Dance around me. flames . . . . . .

סוֹבְבוּנִי לַהַט, אֵשׁ בּוֹעָרֶת,
רַקְדוּ לִי שִׁיר יָחִיד.
זֶה הַזֶּמֶר, זֶה וְאֵין אַחֵר עוֹד,
אֵין אַחֵר עוֹד לְתָמִיד.

טוֹב הַזֶּמֶר עַד אֵין סוֹף,
לֹא יִתַּם, לֹא יַחֲלוֹף.
בִּלְבָבֵנוּ הַקּוֹדֵחַ
מִתְּלָמִים וּמִיָרֵחַ.

סוֹבְבוּנִי ...

TOV LIFROTZ B'SHIR

COME BURST FORTH IN SONG

With spirit

Tov lif - rotz b'-shir O - nim va - ho - ah
Come burst forth in song, Lus - ty and ring - ing.

K'lon ya - mim sh'ho-rim Lim - hot lish - ko - ah. P'rok m'ri
Wipe out shame and wrong, Through the joy of sing - ing. Cast the

ol ka-ved Mi - gav sha - ho-ah, K'naf e - zuz va - gil
yoke of care, From backs low bend-ing, Wings of strength and joy

El al lim - to - ah E - tey al el al al Har Tzi-yon nig-res-
Up - ward a scend-ing. Up-ward up and up - ward, Zi - on be res-

309

al,............ E-ley al, el al, al, Har Tzi-yon, nig-al.....
tored ;........ up-ward up and up-ward, Zi-on be res-tored.....

אֵלַי עָל, אֵל עָל,   פְּרַק מְרִי עַל כָּבֵד   טוֹב לִפְרֹץ בְּשִׁיר –
הַר צִיּוֹן נִגְאָל.   מַגֵּב שָׁחוֹחַ,   אוֹנִים נָכֵחַ
                          כְּנָף עֱזוּז וָגִיל   קָלוֹן יָמִים שְׁחוֹרִים
                          אֵל עָל לִמְתֹחַ.   לִמְחוֹת, לִשְׁכֹּחַ.

HANITA

With Spirit

Lai-la mis-ta-re-a,

Introduction

Esh min he-ha-rim, Ey mi-sham bo-key-a Ze-mer gi-bo-rim......

Esh li-bi hit-hi-ta, Esh li-bi tal-hiv. Laḥ a-ni Ḥa-ni-ta,

Laḥ sa-viv, sa-viv. Ho - ra - te-nu,....... e-res g'vu-ra-te-nu,.......

g'vu - ra - te - nu, e-res g'vu-ra - te - nu.....

Go - - - n'-ni, go-n'-ni a-ley-nu, go - - - n'-ni,

go - n' - ni a - ley - nu, a - - ley - nu. Ki ni - po - la e - lef

E - lef na - - pil, Ad ya - ir yom pe - te. Al ha - rey Ga - lil.

Im hai - ta, hish - ḥi - ta, Yad oi - va - yiḥ baḥ; Od ... na - kim Ḥa - ni - ta

Ho - mo - ta - yiḥ laḥ. Ho - ra - te - nu, ... e - res g'vu - ra - te - nu,
g'vu - ra - te - nu, ... e - res g'vu - ra - te - nu,

Go - - n'-ni, go - n'-ni a - ley - nu; Ah.......

A - ley - nu!

לַיְלָה מִשְׁתָּרֵעַ,   כִּי נָפְלָה אֶלֶף —
אֵשׁ מִן הֶהָרִים,   אֶלֶף נַעֲפִיל,
אֵי מִשָּׁם בּוֹקֵעַ   עַד יָאִיר יוֹם פֶּלֶא
זֶמֶר גִּבּוֹרִים.   עַל הָרֵי נָלִיל.

אֵשׁ לִבִּי הִלְהִיטָה,   אִם הָיְתָה, הֻשְׁחִיתָה
אֵשׁ לִבִּי תַלְהִיב.   יַד אוֹיְבֵיךְ בָּךְ,
לָךְ אֲנִי חֲנִיתָה,   עוֹד נָקִים, חֲנִיתָה,
לָךְ סָבִיב, סָבִיב.   חוֹמוֹתַיִךְ לָךְ.

מקהלה: הוֹרַתָּנוּ, עֶרֶשׂ גְּבוּרָתָנוּ,
גּוֹנְנִי עָלֵינוּ.

Night. Fire lights up the hills as the song of heroes bursts forth. Though the enemy destroy you, O Ḥanita, still shall we build walls about you. O cradle of our strength.

313

AND PERHAPS 'TWAS BUT A DREAM

וְאוּלַי לֹא הָיוּ הַדְּבָרִים מֵעוֹלָם, וְאוּלַי לֹא הִשְׁכַּמְתִּי עִם שַׁחַר לַגָּן, לְעָבְדוֹ בְּזֵעַת אַפִּי. מֵעוֹלָם, בְּיָמִים אֲרֻכִּים וְיוֹקְדִים שֶׁל קָצִיר, מִמְּרוֹמֵי עֲגָלָה עֲמוּסַת אֲלֻמּוֹת לֹא נָתַתִּי קוֹלִי בְּשִׁיר. מֵעוֹלָם לֹא טָהַרְתִּי בִּתְכֵלֶת שׁוֹקְטָה וּבְתֹם שֶׁל כִּנֶּרֶת שֶׁלִּי. הוֹי, כִּנֶּרֶת שֶׁלִּי. הֶהָיִית אוֹ חָלַמְתִּי חֲלוֹם?

316

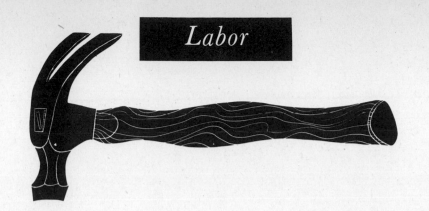

Labor

KADIMA HAPO'EL

di-ma ha-po – el! La, la la la la la la la....... la.................... la

Ka – di-ma ha – a – li – ya!

Forward, worker! Worker, forward!

קָדִימָה, הַפּוֹעֵל! הֵ, הֵ,
קָדִימָה, הַפּוֹעֵל! לַ, לַ...

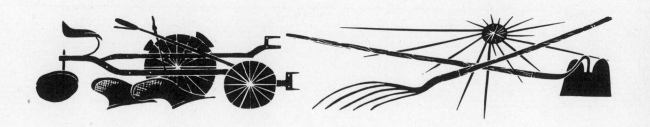

WHO WILL PLOW

Mi yish-tol, yish-tol par-des b'ra-a-na-na? (2)

A-naḥ-nu ha-ḥa-lu-tzim nish-tol et Ra-a-na-na!

Ha-vu la-nu sh'ti-lim, v'nish-tol et Ra-a-na-na.

Who will plant, will plant
An orchard in Ra'anana?
We, Ḥalutzim, will toil and plant
An orange grove in Ra'anana;
Give us trees and give us land,
And we will fructify the sand.

מִי יִשְׁתֹּל, יִשְׁתֹּל פַּרְדֵּס בְּרַעֲנָנָה? (2)
אֲנַחְנוּ הַחֲלוּצִים נִשְׁתֹּל אֶת רַעֲנָנָה!
הָבוּ לָנוּ שְׁתִילִים, וְנִשְׁתֹּל אֶת
רַעֲנָנָה.

מִי יִזְרַע, יִזְרַע שָׂדֶה בְּתֵל-חָי? (2)
אֲנַחְנוּ הַחֲלוּצִים נִזְרַע אֶת תֵּל-חָי!
הָבוּ לָנוּ זֵרְעוֹנִים, וְנִזְרַע אֶת תֵּל-חָי.

va. . . . . Al . . . . . na, al . . . . na, al na tit-ha-mek-na . . . . .

va. . . . . . . Al na, al na, al na, al na al na tit-ha-mek-na Me-a-

Me — a-mal va-a-vo-da. . . . . . . da. . . . . . .

mal . . . . . va-a-vo-da. . . . . da. . . . . .

D. C. al Fine

Dal 𝄋 al Fine

*) *Accompanist: Dal Segno and then D. C. al Fine.*

Daughters, go forth and see the pioneers in the colony. Do not shirk toil and labor.

צְאֶנָה, צְאֶנָה, צְאֶנָה, צְאֶנָה
הַבָּנוֹת, וּרְאֶינָה
חֲלוּצִים בַּמּוֹשָׁבָה.

אַל נָא, אַל נָא, אַל נָא, אַל נָא,
אַל נָא תִּתְחַמֵּקְנָה
מֵעָמָל וַעֲבוֹדָה.

BAMIDBAR

Through the desert shall I be carried on a camel's
back.

בַּמִּדְבָּר יִשָׂאוּנִי
עַל דַּבְּשׁוֹת גְּמַלִּים.
לִי, לִי, לִי, לִי ...
שָׂאוּנִי, שָׂאוּנִי,
בַּמִּדְבָּר שָׂאוּנִי,
לִי, לִי, לִי, לִי ...

SHURU HABITU

SEE THE GLORY OF THIS DAY

ka.......
green............

B' - shal - he - vet y' - ro - ka.........
Crops of rich and flam - ing green.........

אֵת, מַכּוֹשׁ, טוּרִיָה וְקִלְשׁוֹן,
הִתְלַכְּדוּ בְּסְעָרָה.
וְנַדְלִיקָה שׁוּב,
שׁוּב אֶת הָאֲדָמָה
בְּשַׁלְהֶבֶת יְרוֹקָה.

שׁוּרוּ, הַבִּיטוּ וּרְאוּ
מַה גָּדוֹל הַיּוֹם הַזֶּה.
אֵשׁ יוֹקֶדֶת בֶּחָזֶה
וְהַמַּחֲרֵשָׁה
שׁוּב פּוֹלַחַת בַּשָּׂדֶה.

HAVU L'VENIM

BRING THE BRICKS

March

Ha - vu l' - ve - nim, en p'nai laa - mod af re - ga! B'nu ha - ba - na - im, al
Bring, oh bring the bricks; No time to loi - ter here.... Buil - ders; buil - ders build;...

pa-ḥad v'-al ye-ga,..... Kir el kir na-rim lik-raṭ miḥ-shol va-fe-ga. Ku-
know no sloth nor fear........ Raise, oh raise the walls;..... Wor-kers per-se-'vere!..... In

la-nu na-shir him - non bin-yan ar-tze-nu: Bim - kom et - mol yesh
cho-rus let's sing. The buil-der's joy-ous song:.... A new morn is 'wake - ning

la - nu........ ma-har,......... U - v'- ad kol kir,.... b'- ha-nef bin-ya-ne-nu, A-
Af - ter night so long, For all the pain en-dured With ev'ry new foun-da-tion We're

tid a-me-nu hu la-nu..... sa-har... Ha-vu, ha-vu l'- ve-nim,
now as-sured; The...... fu-ture of our na-tion. Bring, and bring, Oh bring the bricks,

הָבוּ לְבֵנִים, אֵין פְּנַאי לַעֲמוֹד אַף
רֶגַע,
בְּנוּ הַבַּנָּאִים אַל פַּחַד וְאַל יֶגַע,
קִיר אֶל קִיר נָרִים לִקְרַאת מִכְשׁוֹל
וָפֶגַע.

כֻּלָּנוּ נָשִׁיר הֶמְנוֹן בִּנְיַן אַרְצֵנוּ:
בִּמְקוֹם אֶתְמוֹל יֵשׁ לָנוּ מָחָר,
וּבְעַד כָּל קִיר, בְּהָנֵף בִּנְיָנֵנוּ,
עָתִיד עַמֵּנוּ הוּא לָנוּ שָׂכָר.

הָבוּ, הָבוּ לְבֵנִים, כְּפָר, מוֹשָׁב וָקֶרֶת,
שִׁירוּ זֶמֶר הַבּוֹנִים, שִׁיר בִּנְיָן וָמֶרֶד!

THE SONG OF WORK AND TOIL

Mi yi-ten la-nu k'sut ba-kor?

U-mi ba-ho-sheh yi-ten or?

Mi ya-a-le ma-yim min ha-bor?

Hoi, l'mi to-da?

מִי יַצִּילֵנוּ מֵרָעָב?

מִי יַאֲכִילֵנוּ לֶחֶם רָב?

מִי יַשְׁקֵנוּ כּוֹס חָלָב?

מקהלה: הוֹי, לְמִי תּוֹדָה?

הוֹי לְמִי בְּרָכָה?

לַעֲבוֹדָה וְלַמְּלָאכָה!

מִי יִתֶּן לָנוּ כְּסוּת בַּקֹר?

וּמִי בַּחשֶׁךְ יִתֶּן אוֹר?

מִי יַעֲלֶה מַיִם מִן הַבּוֹר?

Oh, who shall clothe us when it's cold?

And make the darkness bright as gold?

And make the darkness bright as gold?

And bring up water from the mold?

CHORUS

Who planted trees with fruit to eat?

And pleasant shade against the heat?

And pleasant shade against the heat?

And in the fields has sown the wheat?

CHORUS

So let us work, a busy hive.

Through all the week, while we're alive.

It's hard to strive, it's grand to strive;

And when we've time, the songs arrive:

CHORUS

330

WATCHMAN, WHAT OF THE NIGHT

Not too fast

Ba - a m'nu-ha la - ya - ge - a..... U - mar-go - a le - a -
They who toil are now re - pos - ing,.... Work is done in field and

mel, Lai-la hi-ver mis-ta - re - a Al s'dot E - mek Yiz-r' - el......
dell; Pal-lid night is fast en - clos-ing Soft-ly E-mek Jez-re - el......

Tal mil-ma-ta ul-va-na me-al, Mi-Bet Al-fa ad Na-ha-lal......
T'vo-rah ar-tzi v-tit-ha - lal
Moon-lit dew drops glis-ten as they fall From Bet Al-fa to Na-ha-lal......
Blessed be thou be - - lo-ved of us all

Ma, ma lai-la mi-lel,..... D'ma ma b'-Yiz-r''-el,.....
Watch-man, what of the night,..... Peace reigns si-lent and bright,...

Nu-ma E-mek, e-retz tif-e-ret, A-nu l'-ha mish-me-ret.
Sleep, o E-mek, val-ley of beau-ty, Sleep while we stand on du-ty.

Yam ha-da-gan mit-no-e-a,..... Shir ha-e-der m'-tzal-tzel.....
Zo hi ar-tzi us'-do-te-ha,..... Ze-hu E-mek Yiz-r'-el.......

Corn fields sway in rhyth-mic meas-ure,..... Sweet-ly rings the lamb-kin's bell;...
This the land, this is our treas-ure,..... This is E-mek Jez-re-el.....

בָּאָה מְנוּחָה לַיָּגֵעַ,   יָם הַדָּגָן מִתְנוֹעֵעַ,
וּמַרְגּוֹעַ לֶעָמֵל.   שִׁיר הָעֵדֶר מְצַלְצֵל.
לַיְלָה חִוֵּר מִשְׂתָּרֵעַ   מקהלה: מַה, מַה לַיְלָה מִלֵּיל,   זוֹהִי אַרְצִי וּשְׂדוֹתֶיהָ,
עַל שְׂדוֹת עֵמֶק יִזְרְעָאל.   דְּמָמָה בְּיִזְרְעָאל.   זֶהוּ עֵמֶק יִזְרְעָאל.
טַל מִלְּמַטָּה וּלְבָנָה מֵעַל,   נוּמָה, עֵמֶק, אֶרֶץ תִּפְאֶרֶת,   תְּבָרֵךְ אַרְצִי וְתִתְהַלָּל
מִבֵּית־אַלְפָא עַד נַהֲלָל.   אָנוּ לָךְ מִשְׁמֶרֶת.   מִבֵּית אַלְפָא עַד נַהֲלָל.

HAZORIM B'DIMA

THO' HE PLOW WITH TEARS

Slowly but rhythmically

Hi-ne ge-shem ge-shem ba,..... Bir-ha-to i-mo ra-ba;.....
Pat-ter, pat-ter falls the rain,.... Bring-ing bles-sings in its train,....

Hitzmi-ah e-sev us-dot bar, B'-hol e-mek, al kol har. Ha-zor'-im, ha-zor'-im
Flow-ers, grass and grain that fill Eve-ry val-ley eve-ry hill. Tho he... plow fields with tears

CHORUS

ha-zor'-im b'-dim-a, b'-ri-na, b'-ri-na b'-ri-na yik-tzo-ru.
And sow-ing loud-ly grieves, He shall reap crops with joy and glad-ly ga-ther sheaves..

Be content and make thanksgiving
For the joyous good of living,
A reward for labor's gain
In ripened fruits and golden grain.

CHORUS

הִנֵּה נָשָׁם, נֶשֶׁם בָּא,
בְּרְכָתוֹ עִמּוֹ רַבָּה;
הִצְמִיחַ עֵשֶׂב וּשְׂדוֹת בָּר,
בְּכָל עֵמֶק, עַל כָּל הָר.

מקהלה: הַזּוֹרְעִים (3) בְּדִמְעָה,
בְּרִנָּה (3) יִקְצֹרוּ.

Sa-maḥ lib-ḥa, aḥ va-re-a,
Yesh tag-mul la-zo-re-a.
S'maḥ b'ya-yin, ha-ko-rem
Po-ra-ḥat ge-fen, ge-fen ḥen.

CHORUS

שְׂמַח לִבְּךָ, אָח וָרֵעַ,
יֵשׁ תַּגְמוּל לַזּוֹרֵעַ.
שְׂמַח בְּיַיִן, הַכּוֹרֵם,
פּוֹרַחַת גֶּפֶן, גֶּפֶן חֵן.

מקהלה ....

Ba tor-ḥa gam ha-ko-tzer,
Sh'ma, hak-shev v'hit-ba-ser!
M'ley-a ha-go-ren da-gan rav,
Z'nav shi-bo-let, rosh za-hav.

CHORUS

בָּא תוֹרְךָ גַּם הַקּוֹצֵר,
שְׁמַע, הַקְשֵׁב וְהִתְבַּשֵּׂר:
מָלְאָה הַגֹּרֶן דָּגָן רָב,
זְנַב שִׁבֹּלֶת, רֹאשׁ זָהָב.

מקהלה ....

LO EL SAḤAR

NOT FOR REWARD

Ho-ra s'har-ho-ret, D'vo-ra sh'har-ho-ret! Hal-a, Ad ma-tai? Ad b-li.....dai!
Ho-ra re-sound-ing, E-choes a-bound-ing, On-ward, on-ward men, with the dance we love.

Li ba-mo-le-det ba-yit a-yin,	Not for ourselves the earth we've broken,
Lo bish-vi-li na-ta-ti etz.	Not for ourselves the tree we plant.
T'nu-ni bim-lo gu-fi, k'he-met ya-yin,	Like wine we pour ourselves in loving token
El ad-ma-ta l'hit-na-petz.	Unto the soil new life to grant.

CHORUS

E-rctz no-ga li ge-va va-gai...

לֹא אֵל שָׂכָר הַלֵּב פָּתוּחַ,   מקהלה: אֶרֶץ נֹגַהּ לִי נֶגֶב וָגַיְא,   לִי בַּמּוֹלֶדֶת בַּיִת אַיִן,

לֹא לִתְהִלָּה נָשָׂאנוּ רֹאשׁ.   אַתְּ מַדְלִיקָה לִי אֵשׁ בְּרַגְלַי,   לֹא בִּשְׁבִילִי נָטַעְתִּי עֵץ.

אָנוּ יָצָאנוּ עִם דִּגְלֵי הָרוּחַ,   לַיְלָה פּוֹרֵחַ, רֵיחַ, יָרֵחַ,   תְּנוּנִי בִּמְלֹא גוּפִי, כְּחֶמֶת יַיִן,

אֶת הָאֲוִיר בְּשִׁיר לַחֲרשׁ.   יַס־שָׁמַיִם עָף מֵעָלַי.   אֶל אַדְמָתָהּ לְהִתְנַפֵּץ.

הוֹרָה סְחַרְחֹרֶת, דְּבוֹרָה   מקהלה: ....

שְׁחַרְחֹרֶת!

הָלְאָה! עַד מָתַי? עַד בְּלִי

דַּי!

DAY AFTER DAY

נֵם הַיּוֹם כִּתְמוֹל שִׁלְשׁוֹם,
עַל הַחוֹף עוֹמְדִים בַּחוּרִים מִנְיָן.
לֹא שָׂדֶה לָהֶם, לֹא בַּיִת,
לֹא שָׂדֶה לָהֶם, לֹא בַּיִת וְקִנְיָן.

וּמִי פָקַד, הַרְפֵּה!
פִּי מִי צִוָּה, חֲדוֹל!
הוֹי, בַּחוּרִים! עוֹד הַיּוֹם גָּדוֹל,
תְּנוּ, תְּנוּ חוֹל! הַב זִיפְזִיף, זִיפְזִיף
לַבִּנְיָן!

ONIYOT

March time

O – ni – yot, ... o – ni – yot .... Mi-mer-

ḥak .... hen ba – ot. .... Mi – tza – fon, ... U – mi – da – – –

rom .... M' – vi – ot .... hen ḥa – – lom .... Ha – mon

am .... s'va n' – – dod .... Ku-lam ba – im .... la – a – –

מקהלה: מִי בַּכְּפָר, מִי בָּעִיר –   אֳנִיּוֹת, אֳנִיּוֹת –

לַחֲרשׁ וְלָשִׁיר,   מִמֶּרְחָק הֵן בָּאוֹת.

לִבְנוֹת וּלְהִגָּאֵל   מִצָּפוֹן וּמִדָּרוֹם

בִּמְדִינַת יִשְׂרָאֵל.   מְבִיאוֹת הֵן הֲלוֹם

הַמּוֹדְעָם שֶׁבַּעֲנָדוֹד.

כֻּלָּם בָּאִים לַעֲבֹד.

From north, from south the vessels come, bringing
people weary of wandering. They shall work in the
city and on the farm. Building, singing, in the land
of Israel.

O-ni-yot, o ni-yot

Mi-mer-ḥak hen ba-ot.

Mi-miz-raḥ mi-ma-a'rav

M'vi-ot ka-hal rav

Ba-ḥu-rim, ba-ḥu-rot

Ba-u hey-na liḥ-yot.

CHORUS

אֳנִיּוֹת אֳנִיּוֹת –

מִמֶּרְחָק הֵן בָּאוֹת.

מִמִּזְרָח מִמַּעֲרָב

מְבִיאוֹת קָהָל רָב –

בַּחוּרִים, בַּחוּרוֹת

בָּאוּ הֵנָּה לִחְיוֹת.

מקהלה . . . .

PLADA K'ḤULA

SONG OF THE EMEK

Moderately fast

P'la-da k'ḥu-la....... hem ha-sha-ma-yim,
How blue the flame....... of skies a-bove me,

Kiv-shan a-dom hu l'va-vi.
How red the fur--nace of my heart.

Ha-yom es-rof.....
To-day, with-in

341

ha — lev yik-tzor, Ma — gal ha-ke-shet, mi — ya-a-tzor?
Hearts reap har-vests bright, Our scythes are glow-ing, Who shall stop their might?

Mi — ya-a-tzor? Ey — mek!
Who shall stop their might? Ey — mek!

פְּלָדָה כְּחֻלָּה הֵם הַשָּׁמַיִם,
כְּבִשָּׁן אָדֹם הוּא לִבָּבִי,
הַיּוֹם אֶשְׂרֹף שְׂרִידֵי הַלֵּיל
בְּלַהֲבוֹת שֶׁל מַכְאוֹבִי.

הַיָּד חוֹרֶשֶׁת, הַדָּם גּוֹעֵשׁ,
צִבְעֵי הַקֶּשֶׁת עָלוּ בָאֵשׁ.
אוֹר, אוֹר, אוֹר, אוֹר,
כָּל הָעֵמֶק הוּא שִׁכּוֹר.
הַגִּלְבֹּעַ מִתְנַשֵּׁק עִם הַתָּבוֹר,
הַיָּד חוֹרֶשֶׁת, הַלֵּב יִקְצֹר,
מַגָּל הַקֶּשֶׁת מִי יַעֲצֹר?

עֵמֶק!

343

SHAM B'ERETZ YISRAEL

Very rhythmically

Sham b' - E - retz Yis - ra - el, Sham bi - h'far Y-hez - kel,

Po - a - lim iv - rim ov - dim. Sham b' - E - retz Yis - ra - el, Sham bi -

h'far Y - hez - kel, Po - a - lim iv - rim ov - dim Sham b' -

344

E-retz Yis-ra-el En neh-shal v'en a-tzel Ha-kol ov-dim, ov-dim........ Sham b'

E-retz Yis-ra-el En neh-shal v'en a-tzel Ha-kol ov-dim, ov-dim.........

שָׁם בְּאֶרֶץ יִשְׂרָאֵל
שָׁם בִּכְפַר יְחֶזְקֵאל,
פּוֹעֲלִים עִבְרִים עוֹבְדִים.

שָׁם בְּאֶרֶץ יִשְׂרָאֵל
אֵין נֶחְשָׁל וְאֵין עָצֵל,
הַכֹּל עוֹבְדִים, עוֹבְדִים.

There, in Israel, in K'far Y'hezkel, Jewish workers toil. Workers toil.

KUM BAḤUR ATZEL

In a jolly manner

Kum, ba-ḥur a - tzel, ... v' - tzey la-a-vo – da, ... kum, ba-ḥur a-

tzel, ... v' - tzey la-a-vo – da, ... Kum, ... kum ..... v'-

tzey la-a-vo – da....... da. .... Ku-ku-ri – ku, ku-ku-ri – ku,

ḥatar-n'-gol ka - ra. .... Ku-ku-ri – ku, ku-ku-ri – ku ḥatar-n'-gol ka - ra.

Get up, lazy one, and go out to work. Kukuriku,
Kukuriku, hear the rooster's call.

קוּם, בָּחוּר עָצֵל, וְצֵא לָעֲבוֹדָה.
קוּם, קוּם! וְצֵא לָעֲבוֹדָה.
קוּקוּרִיקוּ, קוּקוּרִיקוּ, הַתַּרְנְגוֹל
קָרָא.

MAYIM, MAYIM

Hey, hey, hey, hey, Ma-yim, ma-yim, ma-yim, ma-yim,

ma-yim, ma-yim, b'-sa-son. ma-yim, ma-yim, b'-sa-son....

Therefore with joy
shall ye draw water
out of the wells of
salvation . . .

הֵי, הֵי, הֵי, הֵי,
מַיִם, מַיִם, מַיִם,
מַיִם, מַיִם בְּשָׂשׂוֹן.

וּשְׁאַבְתֶּם מַיִם בְּשָׂשׂוֹן
מִמַּעַיְנֵי הַיְשׁוּעָה.

מַיִם, מַיִם, מַיִם, מַיִם,
הוֹי מַיִם בְּשָׂשׂוֹן.

HORA AGADATI

JOY WITHIN OUR HEARTS

Rhythmically

Ha-sim-ha ba-lev yo-ke-det, V'-rag-le-nu gil shof-ot,
Joy with-in our hearts is danc-ing, And our feet are keep-ing time,

349

Kol gu - fe - nu la - hat esh V'ha - lev go - esh.
For daunt - - less is our ..... will, And our hearts on fire!

Hal - a kol ma - hov, N' - ga - resh kol pe - ga....
A - way with grief and pain, For hope does sor - row mend, ...

V' - na - sov ha - loh va - sov Ho - ra ad bli sof ki
A - round .... and a - - round a - gain, For Ho - ra has no end! ....

D. C. al Fine

הַשִּׂמְחָה בַּלֵּב יוֹקֶדֶת,
וְרַגְלֵינוּ גִיל שׁוֹפְעוֹת,
כַּךְ נִדְרוֹךְ אַדְמַת מוֹלֶדֶת,
וְנָשִׁירָה: טוֹב לִחְיוֹת!

הַשִּׁירָה בָּרָן זוֹרֶמֶת,
עַל הָרִים וְגֵאָיוֹת.
בְּחָזֵנוּ עוֹד פּוֹעֶמֶת
הַקְּרִיאָה – כִּי טוֹב לִחְיוֹת.

לֹא נֶחְדַּל, כִּי יֵשׁ
עוֹד דֵּי עֹז וָמֶרֶץ.
כָּל גּוּפֵנוּ לַהַט – אֵשׁ!
וְהַלֵּב גּוֹעֵשׁ.

הַלְאָה כָּל מַכְאוֹב,
נְגָרֵשׁ כָּל פֶּגַע
וְנָסֹב הָלוֹךְ וָסֹב
הוֹרָה עַד בְּלִי סוֹף – כִּי ...
..... הַשִּׂמְחָה.

HORA FROM SARID

ARI ARA

MI YIVNE HAGALIL

DEBKA

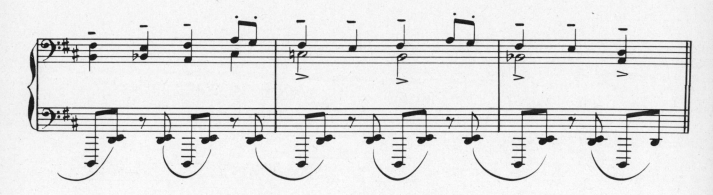

נְרַנְּנָה וְנִשְׂמְחָה בְּכָל יָמֵינוּ

FAVORITE SONGS—OLD AND NEW

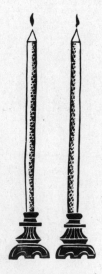

YISRAEL V'ORAITA

*) Second version.

357

ha - le - lu - - yah, ha - le - lu - yah.   ha - le - lu - - yah.

יִשְׂרָאֵל, יִשְׂרָאֵל

וְאוֹרַיְתָא חַד הוא.   וְקֻדְשָׁא. בְּרִיךְ הוא.*

תּוֹרָה אוֹרָה, תּוֹרָה אוֹרָה,

הַלְלוּיָהּ. (4)

Israel and the Torah are one. Torah is light.
Hallelujah.

DUNDAI

Slowly and accented

CHORUS   Solo - as Chorus keeps on with Dundai

Dun - dai, dun - dai,   dun - dai, dun - dai   E - retz Yisra - el   b'-

li To-rah..... Hi k'-guf..... b'-li n'-sha-ma..... Dun-dai, dun-dai, dun-dai,

dun-dai-dai..... dun-dai, dun-dai, dun-dai dun-dai-dai!..... dun-dai-dai.....

Israel without the Torah is like a body without a soul. Children of Israel, learn the Torah and strengthen the nation's soul.

דּוּנְדַּי, דּוּנְדַּי,
דּוּנְדַּי, דּוּנְדַּי.
אֶרֶץ יִשְׂרָאֵל בְּלִי תּוֹרָה
הִיא כְּגוּף בְּלִי נְשָׁמָה.

Yal-de Yis-ra-el,   יַלְדֵי יִשְׂרָאֵל,
Lim-du To-rah,   לִמְדוּ תּוֹרָה,
Ḥaz-ku, am-tzu   חִזְקוּ, אַמְּצוּ
Nish-mat ha-u-ma!   נִשְׁמַת הָאֻמָּה.

OIF'N PRIPITCHOK

BY THE FIRESIDE

ta-ke noḥ a-mol, "Ko-metz A-lef Aw" ....
yet..... once a-gain, "Ko-metz A-lef Aw" ....
"Ko-metz A-lef Aw" / "Ko-metz A-lef Aw"

Le-rent kin-der mit grois ḥey-shek,

A-zoy zog iḥ aiḥ on,

Ver es vet fun aiḥ ke-nen iv-re

Der be-kumt a fon.

CHORUS

Eer vet kin-der el-ter ve-ren,

Vet eer al-leyn fer-shteyn,

Vie feel in die *os-yos* lee-gen tre-ren,

Un vie feel ge-veyn!

CHORUS

When you are older grown,

Oh, my little ones,

You will one day know,

All the tender love and all the burning hope

That in these letters glow.

לָעֶרֶנט קִינְדֶער מִיט גְרוֹיס חֵשֶׁק,

אַזוֹי זָאג אִיך אֵייך אָן,

וֶוער עֶס וֶועט פוּן אֵייך קֶענֶען

עִבְרִי

דֶער בֶּעקוּמט אַ פָאן.

אִיהר וֶועט קִינְדֶער עֶלְטֶער

וֶוערֶען,

וֶועט אִיהר אַלֵיין פַארְשְׁטֶעהן

וִוי פִּיעל אִין דִיא אוֹתִיוֹת לִינֶען

טְרֶערֶען,

אוּן וִויפִּיעל גֶעוֵויין!

אוֹיפֶן פְּרִיפֶּעטשָׁאק בְּרֶענט אַ

פֵּייֶערֶעל

אוּן אִין שטוּב אִיז הֵייס

אוּן דֶער רֶבִּי לָעֶרֶענט קְלֵיינֶע

קִינְדֶערלָאך

דֶעם אַלֶף בֵּית

זֵייטשֶׁע קִינְדֶערלָאך,

גֶעדֶענְקְטשֶׁע טַייֶערֶע,

וָואס אִיהר לָעֶרֶענט דָא.

זָאגְטשֶׁע נָאך אַמָאל,

אוּן טאַקֶע נָאך אַמָאל

„קמץ אַלֶף אָ!"

361

HINEY LO YANUM

*)Go back to 𝄋 and use 2ⁿᵈ End.

The Guardian of Israel neither slumbers nor sleeps.

הִנֵּה לֹא יָנוּם וְלֹא יִישָׁן שׁוֹמֵר
יִשְׂרָאֵל:

Arise, brethren, to your labors! The world depends on work. Our life is work.

Ya ḥai li li, a - ma - li, Ya ḥai li li, a - ma - li. Ya ḥai li li, a - ma - li

U - ru, a - ḥim, al ta - nu - mu! Laa - vo - dat - hem a - na ku - mu.

Ha-o-lam o-med al a-vo-da,   הָעוֹלָם עוֹמֵד עַל עֲבוֹדָה,   מקהלה:
Ha-ri-u, shi-ru v'kol to-da.   הָרִיעוּ, שִׁירוּ בְּקוֹל תּוֹדָה.   יָהּ חַי לִי לִי עֲמָלִי,
Ya ḥai . . .   יָהּ חַי ...

Ha-a-vo-da hi ḥa-ye-nu,   הָעֲבוֹדָה הִיא חַיֵּינוּ,   עוּרוּ, אַחִים, אַל תָּנוּמוּ,
Mi-kol tza-ra to-tzi-e-nu.   מִכָּל צָרָה תּוֹצִיאָנוּ.   לַעֲבוֹדַתְכֶם אָנָא קוּמוּ.
Ya ḥai . . .   יָהּ חַי ...   יָהּ חַי ...

363

AM YISRAEL ḤAI

עַם יִשְׂרָאֵל חַי,
עַד בְּלִי דַי.

Ad b'- li..... dai........ ad b'- li..... dai...... ad b'- li..... dai........

Am Yis-ra-el hai,.... Am Yis-ra-el hai.... Am Yis-ra-el hai..... am Yis-ra-el hai.....

Am Yis-ra-el hai........ Ad b'- li.... dai,...... ad b'- li.... dai..........

ad b'- li..... dai .... Am Yis-ra-el hai, am Yis-ra-el hai............

SHOMER YISRAEL

O Guardian of Israel, guard over the remnant of
Israel. May Israel not be destroyed!

שׁוֹמֵר יִשְׂרָאֵל, שְׁמֹר שְׁאֵרִית
יִשְׂרָאֵל,
אַל יֹאבַד יִשְׂרָאֵל, הָאוֹמְרִים שְׁמַע
יִשְׂרָאֵל.

Sho - mer ... Yis - ra - el, ... sh' - mor ...... sh' - e - rit Yis - ra -

el, ... Al yo - vad Yis - ra - el, al yo - vad Yis - ra - - el ......

Al .... yo - - vad Yis - ra - el, ... al .... yo - - vad Yis - ra - el, ...

al .... yo - - vad Yis - ra - el ..... ha - om - rim Sh'ma Yis - ra - el. ......

OUR SAINTLY RABBIS

With well marked rhythm

*Round — group II begins when group I repeats the stanza.

תָּנוּ, תָּנוּ רַבָּנָן, רַבָּנָן בַּתְרַיְתָא,
בְּרִיךְ הוּא, בְּרִיךְ הוּא, רַחֲמָנָא,
יָהִיב לָנוּ אוֹרַיְתָא.

Y'VOREḤ ES BES YISROEL

May He bless the House of Israel and the House of Aaron. May He bless those who fear Him, the young and the old.

יְבָרֵךְ אֶת בֵּית יִשְׂרָאֵל,
יְבָרֵךְ אֶת בֵּית אַהֲרֹן:
יְבָרֵךְ יִרְאֵי יְיָ,
הַקְּטַנִּים עִם הַגְּדֹלִים:

NIZKE LIROT BANIM

In a jolly manner

La, la, la........

Fine

Niz - ke lir - ot ba - nim, Ba - nim uv'ney ba - nim.... Os-

kim ba - to - rah...... U - va - a - vo - da. Niz - ke lir - ot ba - nim,... ba-

369

D.C. al Fine

nim uv-ney ba-nim.... Os-kim ba-to-rah........ ll-va-a-vo-da.....

D.C. al Fine

May we live to see our children and our children's children engage in the study of the Torah, and in worship.

לְ-לְ-לְ...
נִזְכֶּה לִרְאוֹת בָּנִים,
בָּנִים וּבְנֵי בָנִים
עוֹסְקִים בַּתּוֹרָה
וּבָעֲבוֹדָה.

AGADA

BY THE SEA OF KINNERETH

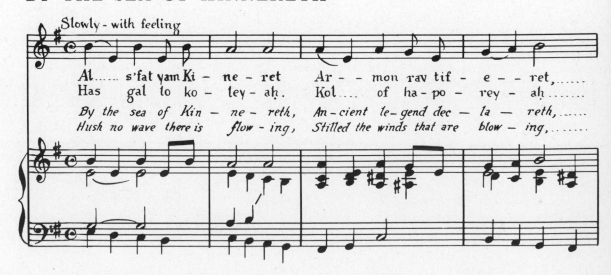

Slowly - with feeling

Al...... s'fat yam Ki — ne — ret   Ar — mon rav tif – e – ret,......
Has gal to ko — tey-ah.   Kol.... of ha-po — rey – ah.......

By the sea of Kin — ne — reth,   An-cient le-gend dec — la — reth,......
Hush no wave there is flow-ing,   Stilled the winds that are blow-ing,.......

370

על שְׂפַת יָם כִּנֶּרֶת

אַרְמוֹן רַב תִּפְאָרֶת,

גַּן אֵל שָׁם נָטוּעַ,

בּוֹ עֵץ לֹא יָנוּעַ.

מִי גָּר שָׁם? רַק נַעַר

כְּעוֹף בְּדִמְי יַעַר;

לוֹמֵד שָׁם תּוֹרָה הוּא

מִפִּיו שֶׁל אֵלִיָּהוּ.

הַס...גַּל לֹא קוֹלֵחַ.

כָּל עוֹף הַפּוֹרֵחַ

עוֹמֵד וְשׁוֹמֵעַ –

תּוֹרַת אֵל בּוֹלֵעַ.

371

M'KOM SHAM ARAZIM

M' - kom sham a-ra-zim v' - a-vim yi-sha-ku; ... V'-

ga-ley ha-yar-den b' - - she-tef yi-tza-ku, M'-kom atz-mot a-vo-tai

nik-b' - ru sha - ma Ud' - mey ha-ma-ka-bim ri - vu ha-a-da-ma, Al

My heart is in the land of my fathers, land where
the cedars rear to the sky, land watered by the blood
of the Maccabees, my land.

ḥof yam hat'-ḥe - let, ... sham kol ha - mu - da - ti, ... 'Sham
ar - tzi, e - retz a - vo - tai. Al ḥof yam hat'-ḥe - let, ... sham
kol ḥa - mu - da - ti, ... Sham ar - tzi e - retz a - vo - tai.

מְקוֹם שָׁם אֲרָזִים וְעָבִים יִשָּׁקוּ;
וְגַלֵּי הַיַּרְדֵּן בְּשֶׁטֶף יָצְקוּ,
מְקוֹם עַצְמוֹת אֲבוֹתַי נִקְבְּרוּ שָׁמָּה,
וּדְמֵי הַמַּכַּבִּים רִוּוּ הָאֲדָמָה,
עַל חוֹף יַם-הַתְּכֵלֶת, שָׁם כָּל חֲמוּדָתִי,
שָׁם אַרְצִי, אֶרֶץ אֲבוֹתַי.

373

ANI MA'AMIN

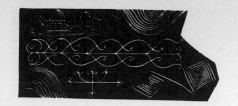

I believe with complete faith in the coming of the Messiah. And though he tarry, still shall I believe and await his coming.

Im ... kol ... ze a - ni ma - a - min, ... Im kol ze ....

a - ḥa - ke ..... lo, ... b' - ḥol yom she-yo — vo.................

A — ni .... ma - a - min....

אֲנִי מַאֲמִין בָּאֱמוּנָה שְׁלֵמָה
בְּבִיאַת הַמָּשִׁיחַ, וְאַף עַל פִּי
שֶׁיִּתְמַהְמֵהַּ, עִם כָּל זֶה אֲנִי מַאֲמִין.
עִם כָּל זֶה אֲחַכֶּה לּוֹ בְּכָל יוֹם
שֶׁיָּבוֹא.

(This song was sung by the DPs who were about to be cremated by the Nazis)

375

SAḤAKI

LAUGH AT ALL MY DREAMS

Saha-ki, saha-ki al haha-lo-mot, Zu a-ni ha-ho-lem sah,......
Laugh at all my dreams my dear-est; Laugh and I re-peat a new........

Saha-ki ki va--a-dam a-amin, Ki o-de-ni ma-amin bah.......
That I still be--lieve in man....... As I still be-lieve in you.......

Saha-ki ki va--a-dam a-amin, Ki o-de-ni ma-amin bah.
That I still be--lieve in man...... As I still be--lieve in you.

Ki od naf-shi d'ror sho-e-fet
Lo m'ḥar-ti-ha l'e-gel paz,
Ki od a-a-min gam ba-a-dam,
Gam b'ru-ḥo, ru-aḥ az.

For my soul is not yet sold
To the golden calf of scorn,
And I still believe in man
And the spirit in him born.

A-a-mi-na gam be-a-tid,
Af im yir-ḥak ze ha-yom,
Aḥ bo ya-vo, yi-s'u sha-lom
Oz u-v'ra-ḥa l'om mi-l'om.

Let the time be dark with hatred,
I believe in years beyond;
Love at last shall bind the people
In an everlasting bond.

On that day shall my own people,
Rooted in its soil arise,
Shake the yoke from off its shoulders
And the darkness from its eyes.

אַאֲמִינָה גַם בָּעָתִיד,   כִּי עוֹד נַפְשִׁי דְּרוֹר שׁוֹאָפָת –   שַׂחֲקִי, שַׂחֲקִי עַל הַחֲלוֹמוֹת,
אַף אִם יִרְחַק זֶה הַיּוֹם.   לֹא מְכַרְתִּיהָ לְעֵגֶל פָּז,   זוּ אֲנִי הַחוֹלֵם שָׂח,
אַךְ בֹּא יָבוֹא – יִשְׂאוּ שָׁלוֹם   כִּי עוֹד אַאֲמִין גַם בָּאָדָם,   שַׂחֲקִי כִּי בָאָדָם אַאֲמִין,
אָז וּבְרָכָה לְאֹם מְלֹאם.   גַם בְּרוּחוֹ, רוּחַ עָז.   כִּי עוֹדֶנִּי מַאֲמִין בָּךְ.

YIGDAL

Fast, like a Hora

I *) Yig-dal E - lo-him ḥai, v'-yish-ta-bah,

II E - ḥod v' - en yo-ḥid, k'yi-ḥu-do,

III Bo - ruḥ a - dey ad

I Nim-tzo v' — en es el m'-tzi-u — so: .... -so.

II Ne — lom v'-gam en sof l'-ah-du-so: .... -so.

III shem t'-hi — lo — so: .... -so.

*) Three part round

*May the Lord be glorified and praised. He is
infinite. He is One, unique in His unity. May His
name be blessed forever.*

יִגְדַּל אֱלֹהִים חַי וְיִשְׁתַּבַּח:
נִמְצָא וְאֵין עֵת אֶל מְצִיאוּתוֹ:
אֶחָד וְאֵין יָחִיד כְּיִחוּדוֹ:
נֶעְלָם וְגַם אֵין סוֹף לְאַחְדּוּתוֹ:
בָּרוּךְ עֲדֵי עַד שֵׁם תְּהִלָּתוֹ:

ROJINKES MIT MANDLEN

IN THE EVENING SHADOWS

Slowly - with feeling

In dem Beys ...... Ha — mik - dosh, in a
In the eve — ning sha - dows, the......

Ah .... Un-ter Yee-de-les vi - - - ge-
Sleep, my lit - tle one, sleep, the soft winds

le, ... Shteyt a klor vais .... tzi - - ge-
blow. ----------------- 'Neath your cra - dle a kid .... stands, white as

le, ... Dos tzi-ge-le iz ge-fo - - rn
snow. ------------------- The lit-tle kid went .... on a

hand - len, -------------------------------------- Dos .... vet
jour - ney, ------------------------------------- And brought .... my

אין דעם בֵּית הַמִקְדָש, אין אַ ווינקל חדר

זיצט די אַלמָנָה בַּת ציון אַליין,

איהר בֶּן יָחִיד'ל, אידעלע, וויגט זי כְּסֵדֶר,

און זינגט איהם צום שלאָפן אַ לידעלע שיין.

אונטער אידעלעס ווינעלע

שטייט אַ קלאָר ווייס ציגעלע.

דאָס ציגעלע איז געפארן האַנדלען,

דאָס וועט זיין דיין בּאַרוף.

ראָזשינקעס מיט מאַנדלעָן.

שלאָף זשע, אידעלע שלאָף!

B'SHADMOT BET LEHEM

IN BETHLEHEM'S FIELDS

Slowly with expression

B' — shad - mot Bet Le — hem, B' - de - reh Ef -

ra - ta, B' - de — reh Ef — — — ra — —

ta, ... A - ley ke - ver k' - du — — mim,

Te - val ma - tza - vet, Te - val ma - tza — —

vet. _____ U - h' - vo ha - tzot lai ___ la, Mey-
e - retz ey - fa ___ ta, Ta - a - le y'fat mar - e, Bet
kiv - ra o - za ___ vet. El Yar - den miz - ra - ha
Du - mam tzo - e - det, Du - mam tzo - e - - -

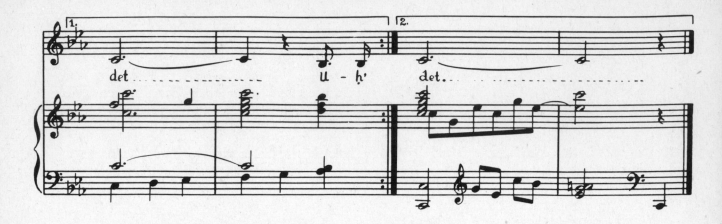

det   u - h'   det..

In Bethlehem's fields, on old Ephrath road,

A monument stands o'er an ancient tomb.

At midnight a mother from her abode,

Arises in the gloom;

To the shores of the Jordan softly she paces,

At the blue, starlit waters, silent, she gazes.

For exiled children she doth mourn,

On each wave her tears are borne.

בְּשַׂדְמוֹת בֵּית לֶחֶם,

בְּדֶרֶךְ אֶפְרָתָה,

עֲלֵי קֶבֶר קְדוּמִים,

תֹּאֱבַל מַצֶּבֶת.

וּכְבֹא חֲצוֹת לַיְלָה,

מֵאֶרֶץ עֵיפָתָה,

תַּעֲלֶה יְפַת מַרְאֶה,

בֵּית קִבְרָהּ עוֹזָבֶת.

אֶל יַרְדֵּן מִזְרָחָה

דוּמָם צוֹעָדֶת.

FLOW ON, JORDAN

Hal - a, Yar-den, hal-a zol! Ye-he-nu ga - le-ha,
Flow on Jor-dan, flow a-long, Waves in cho-rus roar-ing!

Aley g'do-te-ha sh'tof va-gol Hel - at ar - tze-ha;
Flood the banks, with le-gions strong, Sil-ver wa-ters pour-ing.

K'kol...... ra - am har-em kol Ba-ha-mon mey - me-ha, M'-
Now like thun-der, let re-sound Voice of waves in glad-ness!

si - lat Tzi - yon la - nu sol...... Nah-nu a - ha - re-ha!
Lead on Jor-dan, o'er the ground Once we left in sad-ness.

הָלְאָה, יַרְדֵּן, הָלְאָה זוֹל!
יָהֵמוּ גַּלֶּיךָ,
עֲלֵי גְדוֹתֶיךָ שָׁטוֹף נָגַל
חֶלְאַת אַרְצֶךָ;
כְּקוֹל רַעַם הַרְעֵם קוֹל
בַּהֲמוֹן מֵימֶיךָ,
מְסִלַּת צִיּוֹן לָנוּ סַל
נֵחְנוּ אַחֲרֶיךָ!

סקהלה:

הָלְאָה, יַרְדֵּן, הָלְאָה זְרוֹם,
תִּכָּתֵב זֹאת לַדּוֹרוֹת,
כִּי לַיְלָה כַיּוֹם
נֵחְנוּ עַל מִשְׁמָרוֹת.

386

KI MITZIYON

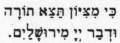

The Torah shall come forth out of Zion, and the word of the Lord from Jerusalem.

כִּי מִצִּיּוֹן תֵּצֵא תוֹרָה
וּדְבַר יְיָ מִירוּשָׁלָיִם.

EVENING PRAYER

Slowly

Great Lord of life who lives in me And lives in all I know, With hap-py thoughts I go to sleep, And while I ... sleep I grow. ... Oh let me wake the com-ing morn More strong and brave and

389

bright, The while you guard with lov-ing care All those I love to-night.

HELM SONG

To top--sy-tur-vy town,.... tur--vy town...... To

tur--vy town..... On a lit-tle brown po-ny, a lit-tle boy rides O-ver

cob-ble stone roads, thru strange coun-try sides; He rides to and fro,.... And he

D.C. al Fine

rides up and down, Asks milk-maids and black-smiths how far 'tis to town............

D.C. al Fine

His grandfather told him that would he be wise
He must see the fool's town with his very own eyes;
See Jews catch the moon in a bucket for cheese,
And find the next night that moon stuck in the trees —
   To topsy-turvy town, turvy town. (2)

See the simpleton settling high matters of state;
The rabbi a-scratching his dubious pate,
Watch the baker knead rolls out of dough made of lime,
Since it never turned sour, and kept a long time —
   To topsy-turvy town, turvy town. (2)

So into the hamlet the little boy rides —
Oh, even his pony is holding its sides!
The little boy smiles to the Jews of the realm,
Nods right and nods left to the burghers of Helm,
   To topsy-turvy town, turvy town. (2)

RABBI SIMEON AND THE JEWELS

master stern-ly ans-wered "God com-mands not theft but thrift."

D.C. al Fine

TO A STAR

Moderato

O lit-tle star, O gen-tle star, Hide not from me in sad-ness! Peep

in my win-dow from on high, Bring tid-ings... full of glad-ness.

Come, twin-kle, wink, and tell me, star, what are the che-rubs do-ing. Are they

D.C. al Fine

play-ing there with balls of fire, And light-ning-shafts per-su-ing? ....

D.C. al Fine

Does David play upon his harp
In sacred exaltation?
Or does he whet his sword to fight
And free his fettered nation?

EARLY WILL I SEEK THEE

Simply

Ear - ly will I seek Thee, God, my re - fuge strong;......
What this frail heart drea - meth, And my tongue's poor speech,......

Late pre - pared to meet Thee With my eve - ning song.......
Can they e - ven dis - tant to Thy great - ness reach?......

Though un - to Thy great - ness I with tremb - ling soar,......
Be - ing great in mer - cy.... Thou wilt not des - pise.......

Yet my in - most think - ing Lies Thine eyes be - fore....
Prais - es which till death's hour From my soul shall rise....

AT THE DAWN I SEEK THEE

Slowly

At the dawn...... I...... seek Thee, re-fuge rock........ sub-
And with al,......... what is it heart and tongue...... can......

lime;......... Set my prayer be-fore Thee in the morn-ing,......
do?......... What is this...... my strength, and what is e - - ven......

And my prayer.... at e-ven time. I be - fore...... Thy great-ness stand
this, The spir - - it in me, too? But, in - deed,...... man's sing-ing may

and........ am a - fraid;......... All my sec - - ret thoughts Thine
seem........ good to Thee;......... So I praise Thee, sing-ing,

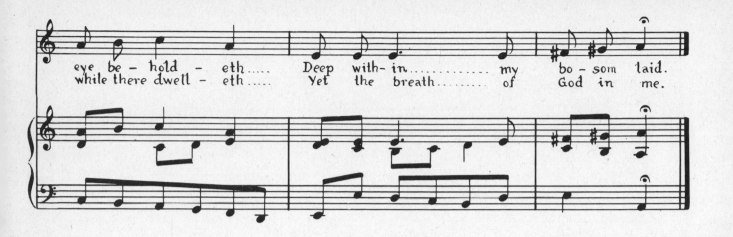

THE LORD IS MY STRENGTH

die.... but live,............ and de – clare the works....... of .... the

1. Lord.............. And de –
2. Lord,........... of the Lord................

Fine

clare the works of the Lord, the works of the Lord,..... of the Lord,.....

Da Capo dal segno al "Fine"

.... the works........ of the Lord,......... of the Lord.......

Da Capo dal segno al "Fine"

GOD SUPREME!

God su preme! to..... Thee we pray Let our lips be

taught to say, Whe-ther good or ill.... may flow, Hea-ven-ly Fa-ther

be ...... it so, Hea-ven-ly Fa-ther be.... it so....

Thou alone dost best decide
Whatsoe'er shall us betide;
Be our station high or low,
Heavenly Father be it so. (2)

SOUND THE LOUD TIMBREL

splen-did and brave, How vain was their boasting, the Lord hath but spok-en, And

char-iots and horse-men are sunk in the wave. Sound the loud... tim-brel o'er

E - gypt's dark sea! The Lord hath triumphed, His peo-ple are free. peo-ple are free.

[May also be sung on Passover].

THE ARK

The rain is rain-ing day and night! With in the Ark, O what, a sight! No-ah is the Cap-tain, and ev-'ry one a-board Is hap-py that he lis-ten'd to the or-der of the Lord. The an-i-mals are hap-py, the an-i-mals are good, A-

sail-ing in the Ark that No-ah made of wood; Rest-ing there in safe-ty, iu

com-fort and in love, The el-e-phant, the ti-ger, and the li-on and the dove.

The rain was raining day and night
And not a dry spot was in sight.
Noah sent the raven out, the raven, Oh, so black,
The naughty raven flew away and never did come back.

CHORUS:
The animals are happy, the animals are good.
A-sailing in the Ark that Noah made of wood;
Resting there in comfort, in safety and in love,
The leopard, and the zebra, and the lion and the dove!

When Noah saw it clear above,
He sent the little snow-white dove,
And when the dove came back from flying far away,
An olive branch was in its mouth, Oh, what a happy day!

CHORUS:
The animals were happy, the animals were good.
A-coming from the Ark that Noah built of wood;
Coming out together in sunshine and in love,
With thanks to Captain Noah and the snow-white dove!

THE TOWER OF BABEL

Moderato

O, I'll sing you a sto-ry that's fun-ny and sad 'Bout the sil-li-est peo-ple the world ev-er had, O, they tried to reach God, but none of them could fly, So they build-ed a tow-er that reached up so high.

Bang! went the ham-mer, and chop! went the wood, And click! went the brick where the brick lay-ers stood; And each man was work-ing as best he was a-ble To reach up to God with the tow-er of Ba-bel!

So they built and they built the tower so tall,
Till they couldn't see down to earth there at
 all.
And the harder they worked, and worked,
 night and day,
The further the heavens seemed drawing
 away.

CHORUS

Then something strange happened, and no-
 body knew
What anybody else was planning to do,
And no one understood the speech that was
 spoken,
And everything got mixed and the tower was
 broken.

CHORUS

FOOLISH LOT

Lively   Voice

Lot, Lot, fool-ish man, Went to live in So-dom Town. Run! run! As fast as you can The wicked town is burn-ing down. Lot, Lot, fool ish Lot! I am glad that I am not As fool-ish, as fool-ish.... As Lot, Lot, Lot.

The wife of Lot, she forgot

The angel's orders not to halt,

She turned around, and on the spot

The wife of Lot was turned to salt.

CHORUS:

Lot, Lot, foolish Lot!

I am glad that I am not

As foolish, as foolish

As the wife of Lot.

ELIEZER AND REBECCA

Good Rebecca, sweet Rebecca

Went to fetch some fresh well water;

O she was a lovely maiden

And she was Bethuel's daughter.

Eliezer, Eliezer

With his camels heavy laden,

At the well met sweet Rebecca;

For a drink he begged the maiden.

And Rebecca, sweet Rebecca

From her brimming pitcher gave

Drink to master and to slave.(2)

Eliezer, Eliezer

Never met in all his life

A kinder maid than sweet Rebecca;

So she became good Isaac's wife.

THE LADDER OF THE ANGELS

Moderato

When Ja-cob fled
night time came

from E-sau's wrath .... Re-bec-ca told her best loved
and the bright moon beamed .... With a sto--ny pillow 'neath his

son .... Toward A-ra-my to take.... his path..... He
head .... O what a won-der-ful dream he dreamed a-

1.
walked un-til the set of sun.......... When

2.
sleep-ing here on a sto-ny

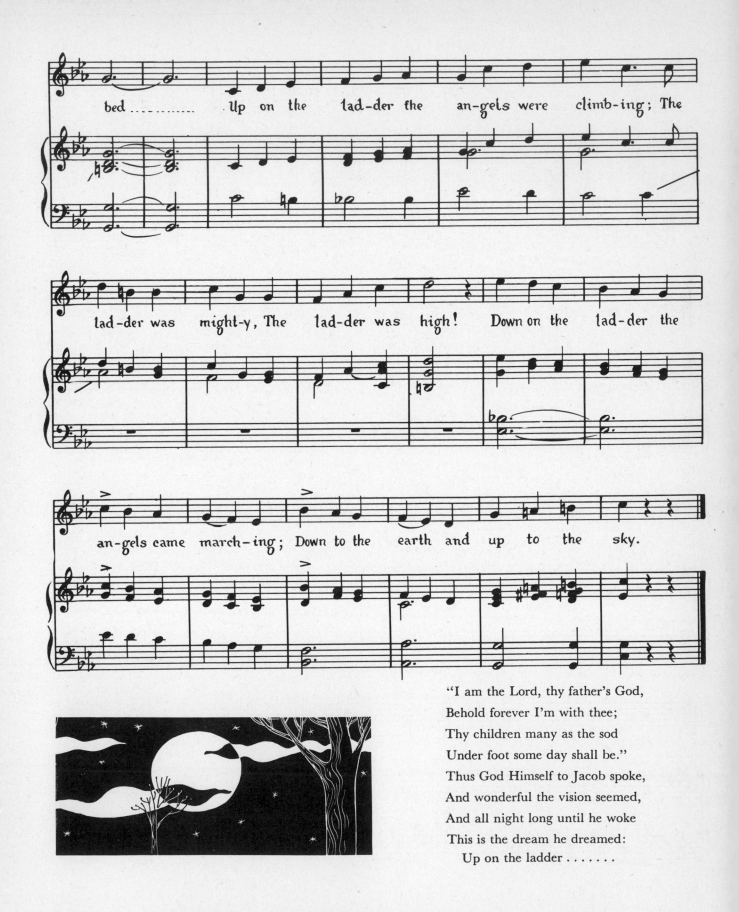

bed . . . . Up on the lad-der the an-gels were climb-ing; The

lad-der was might-y, The lad-der was high! Down on the lad-der the

an-gels came march-ing; Down to the earth and up to the sky.

"I am the Lord, thy father's God,
Behold forever I'm with thee;
Thy children many as the sod
Under foot some day shall be."
Thus God Himself to Jacob spoke,
And wonderful the vision seemed,
And all night long until he woke
This is the dream he dreamed:
    Up on the ladder . . . .

JOCHEBED'S SONG

Slowly - with feeling

In this bas - ket goes my child,...... And my eyes with tears are dim.......... In the ri - ver.... goes my child,...... And all my love goes... out with him, In the ri - ver goes my child,......... And all my love goes out with him.........

Here I lay him, Oh, so tenderly,

Darling child, Oh, do not cry.

Oh, I love my dear child so,

How could I live, if he should die?

River, river, take my child,

Keep him safe from harm and pain;

River, when the danger's o'er,

Oh, give him back to me again.

MOSES AND THE BURNING BUSH

Pastoral quality

1 On the mount-ain side there graz-es Peace-ful-ly a flock of sheep. The shep-herd
2 The shep-herd Mo-ses from the pas-ture Sees the un-con-sum-ing flame. And he

sees; a great flame blaz-ing In the bush-es hid-den deep...... And the
hears with ho-ly rap-ture An an-gel speak-ing in God's name. "Have no

sod!.... I have come.... un-to this place, And in fear...... I hide my face.... Lest I look.... Lest I look.... up-on... the liv — ing God.

MOSHE VIHOSHUA

Slowly

Ha - yom i -lan Bo-ḥe ba - ru - aḥ...... Ma-
du-a hu Bo-ḥe, ma-du - a?..... Mo - she ha-taḥ...... Lo shav, lo shav...... V'
en mo - re ...... V' - - en od rav........ A - tzuv o -med Lo Y' - ho-

Po en mo-re	Pit-om za-raḥ	פֹּה אֵין מוֹרָה	הַיּוֹם אִילֵן
V'en na-vi —	Lo, li-ho-shu-a,	וְאֵין נָבִיא —	בּוֹכֶה בָּרוּחַ.
Ha-am la-a-retz	Or rav — v'lo	הָעָם לָאָרֶץ	מַדּוּעַ הוּא
Mi ya-vi?	Ha-kol ya-du-a:	מִי יָבִיא?	בּוֹכֶה, מַדּוּעַ?
A-ni tza-ir,	To-rat Mo-she	אֲנִי צָעִיר,	מֹשֶׁה הָלַךְ,
Kim-at od na-ar —	Li ha-maf-te-aḥ.	כִּמְעַט עוֹד נַעַר —	לֹא שָׁב, לֹא שָׁב —
U-mi yif-taḥ	Aḥ-nis la-a-retz	וּמִי יִפְתַּח	וְאֵין מוֹרָה
La-am ha-sha-ar?	Am ya-ge-a.	לָעָם הַשַּׁעַר? —	וְאֵין עוֹד רַב.
		פִּתְאֹם זָרַח	עָצוּב עוֹמֵד
		לוֹ, לִיהוֹשֻׁעַ,	לוֹ יְהוֹשֻׁעַ,
		אוֹר רַב — וְלוֹ	עֵינָיו דּוֹמְעוֹת,
		הַכֹּל יָדוּעַ:	לִבּוֹ קָרוּעַ:
		— תּוֹרַת מֹשֶׁה	מֹשֶׁה הָלַךְ —
		לִי הַמַּפְתֵּחַ.	וּמִי חָכָם,
		אַכְנִיס לָאָרֶץ	אֲשֶׁר יוֹלִיךְ,
		עַם יָגֵעַ.	יוֹרֶה הָעָם?

Moses is gone, never to return. Joshua weeps.
Who will teach the people, who will bring them to
the land? Suddenly a great light shone on Joshua,
and he knew all the teachings of Moses. I shall
bring my weary people into the land.

MOSES ON MOUNT NEBO

Moderately slow

When Mo-ses..... led the Is-rael-ites Through des-erts filled with

sand,.......... And brought them near, to taste de-lights...... In

milk and ho-ney..... land;...... He knew be-fore him was the home,.... Of

Is-rael's wand-er-ing band..................... And on - - ly Mo-ses

dare not come..... To live with-in..... the land. O beau—·te—ous

Jor-dan, love-ly stream;...... O land...... be-neath....... me

spread,...... O Land..... of Pro—mise, of my dream,...

...... That I shall nev—er tread............ O hap—py

home of Is-ra-el,........... O land of pro-mise fare thee well,........... O hap--py home of Is-ra-el,..... fare the well. O..... fare....... thee....... well.............................

And God's voice speaks to him once more,
"This land so great and fair,
O unto Israel's seed I swore
A home for them for e'er."
And now he stands with longing eyes,
And heart that's full of love.
The Promised Land beneath him lies,
He views it from above.

CHORUS

SHMUEL HAKATAN

When Samuel was a child, his mother made him a robe: "You shall wear this robe," she said, "and serve the Lord." She brought Samuel to Eli the priest. Eli was an old man and sad. Samuel wept, "Take me home, mother." At night he heard a voice, "Samuel, Samuel!" But the child did not know that the Lord was calling him.

מְעִיל תָּפְרָה
אִמָּא לִשְׁמוּאֵל.
אָמְרָה לִבְנָהּ:
תִּהְיֶה כַּהֵרְאֵל,

תִּלְבַּשׁ זֶה הַמְּעִיל,
אֱלֹהִים תַּעֲבֹד. –
וְהַיֶּלֶד שְׁמוּאֵל
קָטָן אָז מְאֹד.

לֹא הֵבִין דָּבָר
מִדִּבְרֵי הָאֵם –
קָטָן הוּא מְאֹד,
מְשַׂחֵק וְחוֹלֵם.

הֱבִיאָה אוֹתוֹ
אֶל עֵלִי הַכֹּהֵן –
וְעֵלִי כֹה עָצוּב,
עָצוּב וְזָקֵן.

בָּכָה הַתִּינוֹק:
– אֵיךְ אֶהְיֶה פֹּה, אֵיךְ?
הַבַּיְתָה, אִמָּא,
הַבַּיְתָה אֵלֵךְ!

בַּלֵּיל נִשְׁמַע קוֹל:
– שְׁמוּאֵל, שְׁמוּאֵל!
לֹא הֵבִין הַתִּינוֹק,
כִּי קָרָא לוֹ אֵל.

בָּכָה הַתִּינוֹק,
בָּכָה וּבָכָה:
– נוֹרָא הַמָּקוֹם!
הַבַּיְתָה אֵלְכָה.

DAVID HARO'E

422

הָיָה הָיָה
רוֹעֶה צָעִיר.
גָּדוֹל הָיָה
כֹּחוֹ בַּשִּׁיר.

גַּם לֵב אָדָם
עָצוּב שִׂמַּח –
שָׁעָה קַלָּה
עָצְבּוֹ שָׁכַח.

מִיַּעַר-עַד
אִם בָּא הַזְּאֵב
לִטְרֹף טַרְפּוֹ
כִּי הוּא רָעֵב –

כִּנּוֹר הָיָה
לוֹ, לָרוֹעֶה,
וּבוֹ שִׂמַּח
אֶת לֵב הַשֶּׂה.

וְקֶסֶם רַב
בּוֹ, בַּכִּנּוֹר,
וְכֹחַ רַב
בְּכָל מִזְמוֹר.

לַמַּנְגִּינָה
הִקְשִׁיב הַקְשֵׁב,
מִיָּד שָׁכַח
כִּי הוּא רָעֵב.

There was once a young shepherd who had the gift of song. Playing upon his harp, he could calm the breast of man and beast. Even the wolf, who came out of the forest to prey on the sheep, forgot his hunger when he heard the songs of David.

424

KING SOLOMON

Moderately

A wise old king was Sol-o-mon For .... for-ty..... years he reigned, ... And judged his peo-ple truth-ful-ly, ... His wis-dom... was far-famed. .... He must have had his...... troub-les, ... tho'! For

one thou-sand wives had ..... he ; .... I won - der how he know them all ......

My ! what a mem-o - - ry ! .... Oh, what a ..... mem-o - - ry ! ....

TALMID ḤARUTZ

Slowly

Tal -

hlal?.. Hi - lel.......... um - lal, um - lal, um - lal.........

Ya-mim ra-bim	יָמִים רַבִּים	תַּלְמִיד חָרוּץ
Da-og da-ag.	דָּאֹג דָּאַג.	הָיָה הַלֵּל;
Liv-sof a-la	לִבְסוֹף עָלָה	לָמַד בַּיּוֹם,
Lo al ha-gag	לֹא עַל הַגַּג	קָרָא בַּלֵּיל.
Shel bet ha-se-fer	שֶׁל בֵּית הַסֵּפֶר	עָנִי הָיָה,
V'ya-shav	וְיָשַׁב	עָנִי מְאֹד.
L'yad ha-lon	לְיַד חַלּוֹן,	בְּבֵית־הַסֵּפֶר
L'mul ha-rav;	לְמוּל הָרַב;	אֵיךְ לִלְמֹד —
V'hol ha-yom	וְכָל הַיּוֹם	וְכֶסֶף אֵין לוֹ
Sha-ma mi-piv	שָׁמַע מִפִּיו	כְּלָל וּכְלָל.
Div-re To-rah —	דִּבְרֵי תוֹרָה —	הַלֵּל אֻמְלָל,
Hik-shiv, hik-shiv.	הִקְשִׁיב, הִקְשִׁיב.	אֻמְלָל, אֻמְלָל.
Ya-rad ha-she-leg	יָרַד הַשֶּׁלֶג	
Al Hil-lel,	עַל הַלֵּל,	
Ki-sa o-to	כִּסָּה אוֹתוֹ	
Gam yom, gam lel.	גַּם יוֹם, גַּם לֵיל.	
V'lo hir-gish	וְלֹא הִרְגִּישׁ	
Hil-lel ba-kor.	הַלֵּל בַּקֹּר —	
To-rah lo hom,	תּוֹרָה לוֹ חֹם,	
To-rah lo or . . .	תּוֹרָה לוֹ אוֹר . . .	

Hillel was a diligent student, but so poor that he had no money to pay for his studies at school. Hillel went up to the roof and pressed his ear against the window. All day he listened to the words of the Torah. The snow came down and covered him. But Hillel did not feel the cold. The Torah was his warmth and light.

YOḤANAN BEN ZAKAI

Naf - sho...... va - kaf Ya - tza ha - sha - -
ar............ Ba - ir........ Yav - ne.... Ba - ir ....
Yav - ne Ya - sad bet se - - - - fer .... v' -
lien hi - tzil gam am, Gam.... se - - - fer.............

רָאָה: הַכֹּל עָזַב הָעִיר בָּעִיר יַבְנֶה
נִשְׂרָף לְאֵפֶר. בְּיוֹם הַסַּעַר, יָסַד בֵּית־סֵפֶר –
אָמַר: – אֵלֵךְ, נַפְשׁוֹ בְכַפּוֹ – וְכָן הִצִּיל
אַצִּיל הַסֵּפֶר. יָצָא הַשַּׁעַר. גַּם עָם, גַּם סֵפֶר.

He saw everything burned to ashes. "I shall save the Book," he said. Taking his life in his hands he stole out of the gates. In the city of Yavneh he founded a school, thus saving both his people and the Book.

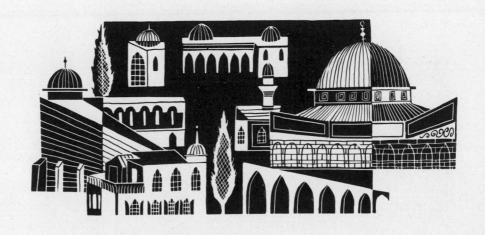

BARUḤ HABA

SONG OF DEDICATION

Moderato—with feeling

Bo - ruh ha - bo b'-
This child we ded - i -

shem A - do - noi b' - rah - nu - hem mi - bes A - do - noi. El A - do - noi va -
cate to.... Thee, O God of grace and pu - ri - ty. Shield it from sin and

yo - er.... to - nu is - ru hag ba - vo - sim ad kar - nos ha - miz - be - ah. Ey -
threaten - ing wrong.. And let Thy.... love... its life pro - - - long.........

432

li a to vo de ho E lo-hai a-ro ma me ho Ho-
may Thy spir-it gent-ly draw Its will-ing soul to keep Thy law, May

du la-do-noi ki tov ki vo-lom has do.
vir-tue, pi-e-ty, and truth Dawn e-ven with its dawn-ing youth.

rit.

אֵלִי אַתָּה וְאוֹדֶךָ,
אֱלֹהַי אֲרוֹמְמֶךָ,
הוֹדוּ לַאדֹנָי כִּי טוֹב
כִּי לְעוֹלָם חַסְדּוֹ.

בָּרוּךְ הַבָּא בְּשֵׁם אֲדֹנָי,
בֵּרַכְנוּכֶם מִבֵּית אֲדֹנָי.
אֵל אֲדֹנָי וַיָּאֶר לָנוּ אִסְרוּ חַג
בַּעֲבֹתִים עַד קַרְנוֹת הַמִּזְבֵּחַ.

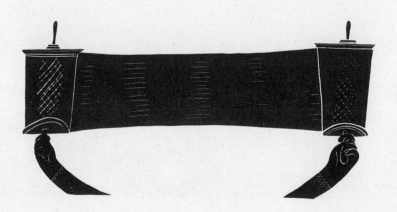

GIVER OF ALL

Slowly

O Fath-er, Thou who giv-est all the boun-ty of Thy per-fect love; .... We

thank Thee that up--on us fall Such ten-der bles-sings from a-bove.

We thank Thee for the gift of home,
For mother's love and father's care;
For friends and teachers, all who come
Our joys and hopes and fears to share.

For faith to conquer doubt and fear,
For love to answer every call,
For strength to do, and will to dare,
We thank Thee, O Thou Lord of all.

ALMIGHTY GOD

Almighty God protect Your children

When they cry in sore distress.

Give us of Your bounteous blessings,

Grant us peace and happiness.

אַל כַּבִּיר לָךְ שִׁירִים שָׁרִים

קוֹצְרֵי בּוֹר בְּצָהֳרֵי יוֹם.

אִסְפוּ אַחִים הָעֳמָרִים,

טֶרֶם יִשְׁקַע שֶׁמֶשׁ רָם.

EYES OF THE FACE I LOVE

free!..... For him who sets a peo-ple free Like Mo-ses, sent by God,... To smite, to

smite the House of.... Bond - - age with His won - der wor - king rod.............

Who led the slaves of Egypt out
     To freedom and new life,
Like you, abiding meek but firm
     In peril or in strife.

And when he brought the Word of God
     From Sinai's craggy height;
Behold, his face was like the sun!
     It shone with beams of light!

And that must be the holy light,
     The light from God above,
That shines in Lincoln's tender eyes,
     Eyes of the face I love.

THE COLOSSUS

side the gol – den door . . . .

HATIKVAH

Majestically

Kol... od ba-le-vav p'ni – – – ma... ne-fesh ye-hu-di ho – mi – ya.....u-

l'fa – tey miz-rah ka – di – ma.... a –yin l'–Tzi-on tzo – fi – a............

od lo av-da tik-va-tey-nu..... ha - tik-va sh'not al-pa-yim.........

li-yot am haf-shi b' - ar-tzey-nu e-retz Tzi-yon vi-ru-sha-la-yim.....

So long as the heart of the Jew beats and his eye is turned to the East, so long does our ancient hope of returning to Zion still live.

כָּל עוֹד בַּלֵּבָב פְּנִימָה
נֶפֶשׁ יְהוּדִי הוֹמִיָּה,
וּלְפַאֲתֵי מִזְרָח קָדִימָה
עַיִן לְצִיּוֹן צוֹפִיָּה.

עוֹד לֹא אָבְדָה תִקְוָתֵנוּ,
הַתִּקְוָה שְׁנוֹת אַלְפַּיִם,
לִהְיוֹת עַם חָפְשִׁי בְּאַרְצֵנוּ,
בְּאֶרֶץ צִיּוֹן וִירוּשָׁלַיִם.

THE STAR-SPANGLED BANNER

proof thro' the night that our flag was still there! O......... say, does the..... star-span-gled ban-ner still wave.. O'er the land of the free, and the home of the brave?

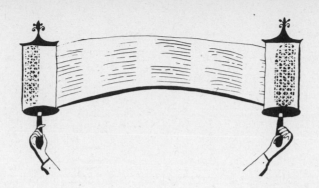

BIRHOT HATORAH

Bo-r'—hu es A-do-noi ha-m'-vo-roh: Bo-

ruh A-do-noi ha-m'vo-roh l'-lom vo-ed: Bo - ruh a-to A-do-noi e-lo-

Bo - ruh a-to A-do-noi e-lo-

he-nu me-leh ho-o-lom, a-sher bo-har bo-nu mi-kol ho-a-mim v'-no-san

he-nu me-leh ho-o-lom, a-sher no-san lo-nu to-ras.... e-mes v'ha-yey o-

lo nu es to-ro-so. Bo-ruh a-to A-do-noi no-sen ha-to-roh.

1om,... no-ta b'so-he-nu

בָּרְכוּ אֶת־יְיָ, הַמְבֹרָךְ:

בָּרוּךְ יְיָ, הַמְבֹרָךְ לְעוֹלָם וָעֶד:

בָּרוּךְ אַתָּה, יְיָ, אֱלֹהֵינוּ, מֶלֶךְ
הָעוֹלָם, אֲשֶׁר בָּחַר־בָּנוּ, מִכָּל־
הָעַמִּים, וְנָתַן־לָנוּ, אֶת־תּוֹרָתוֹ.
בָּרוּךְ אַתָּה, יְיָ, נוֹתֵן הַתּוֹרָה:

בָּרוּךְ אַתָּה, יְיָ, אֱלֹהֵינוּ, מֶלֶךְ
הָעוֹלָם, אֲשֶׁר נָתַן־לָנוּ, תּוֹרַת אֱמֶת,
וְחַיֵּי עוֹלָם, נָטַע בְּתוֹכֵנוּ. בָּרוּךְ
אַתָּה, יְיָ, נוֹתֵן הַתּוֹרָה:

CANTILLATION OF THE TORAH

444

וַיֹּאמֶר אֱלֹהִים יְהִי אוֹר וַיְהִי אוֹר:
וַיַּרְא אֱלֹהִים אֶת הָאוֹר כִּי טוֹב
וַיַּבְדֵּל אֱלֹהִים בֵּין הָאוֹר וּבֵין
הַחֹשֶׁךְ:
וַיִּקְרָא אֱלֹהִים לָאוֹר יוֹם וְלַחֹשֶׁךְ
קָרָא לָיְלָה וַיְהִי עֶרֶב וַיְהִי בֹקֶר
יוֹם אֶחָד:

בְּרֵאשִׁית בָּרָא אֱלֹהִים אֵת הַשָּׁמַיִם
וְאֵת הָאָרֶץ:
וְהָאָרֶץ הָיְתָה תֹהוּ וָבֹהוּ וְחֹשֶׁךְ עַל
פְּנֵי תְהוֹם וְרוּחַ אֱלֹהִים מְרַחֶפֶת
עַל פְּנֵי הַמָּיִם:

BIRḤOT HAHAFTARAH

Bo — ruḥ a — to...... A-do-noi e-lo-he-nu me-leḥ ho-o-lom,.... a-
sher bo-ḥar bin-vi-im to-vim, v'-ro — tzo v'-div-re-hem, ha-ne-e-mo-
rim be-e-mes:.... Bo — ruḥ a — to............... A-do-
noi,......... ha-bo — her...... ba-to-ro........... uv'-Mo-
she... av-do.... uv'-Yis-ro-el...... a-mo, uv-in-vi-ey ho-e-mes vo — tze-dek.

בָּרוּךְ אַתָּה, יְיָ, הַבּוֹחֵר בַּתּוֹרָה
וּבְמֹשֶׁה עַבְדּוֹ וּבְיִשְׂרָאֵל עַמּוֹ
וּבִנְבִיאֵי הָאֱמֶת וָצֶדֶק:

בָּרוּךְ אַתָּה, יְיָ, אֱלֹהֵינוּ, מֶלֶךְ
הָעוֹלָם, אֲשֶׁר בָּחַר בִּנְבִיאִים טוֹבִים
וְרָצָה בְדִבְרֵיהֶם, הַנֶּאֱמָרִים בֶּאֱמֶת:

Bo - ruḥ.......... a - to A - do - noi e - lo - he - nu me - leḥ ho - o - lom, tzur kol ho - o - lo - mim, tza - dik b'- ḥol ha - do - ros, ho - El ha - ne - e - mon,...... ho - o - mer v'- o - se,..... ham'da - ber u - m'ka - yem she - kol d'vo - rov..... emes vo - tze - dek Nee - mon.......... a - to hu A - do - noi E - lo - he - nu, v'- ne - e - mo - nim d'- vo - re - ḥo, v'- do - vor e - ḥod.... midvo - re - - ḥo o - ḥor lo yo - shuv re - kom ki El me - leḥ ne - e - mon v'- ra - ḥa - mon o - to, bo - ruḥ a - to A - do - noi, ho - El ha - ne - e - mon...... b'- ḥol d'vo - rov. Ra - ḥem........ al tzi - yon, ki hi bes ḥa - ye - nu, v'- la - a - lu - vas ne - fesh to - shi - a bimḥe - ro v'- yo - me - nu. Bo - ruḥ a - to A - do - noi m'sa - me - aḥ Tzi - yon...... b'- vo - ne - ho.

רַחֵם עַל־צִיּוֹן, כִּי הִיא בֵּית חַיֵּינוּ,
וְלַעֲלוּבַת נֶפֶשׁ תּוֹשִׁיעַ בִּמְהֵרָה
בְיָמֵינוּ: בָּרוּךְ אַתָּה, יְיָ, מְשַׂמֵּחַ צִיּוֹן
בְּבָנֶיהָ:

נֶאֱמָן אַתָּה הוּא יְיָ אֱלֹהֵינוּ וְנֶאֱמָנִים
דְּבָרֶיךָ וְדָבָר אֶחָד מִדְּבָרֶיךָ אָחוֹר
לֹא יָשׁוּב רֵיקָם כִּי אֵל מֶלֶךְ נֶאֱמָן
וְרַחֲמָן אָתָּה. בָּרוּךְ אַתָּה יְיָ הָאֵל
הַנֶּאֱמָן בְּכָל־דְּבָרָיו:

בָּרוּךְ אַתָּה, יְיָ, אֱלֹהֵינוּ, מֶלֶךְ
הָעוֹלָם, צוּר כָּל־הָעוֹלָמִים, צַדִּיק
בְּכָל־הַדּוֹרוֹת, הָאֵל הַנֶּאֱמָן, הָאוֹמֵר
וְעוֹשֶׂה, הַמְדַבֵּר וּמְקַיֵּם, שֶׁכָּל־
דְּבָרָיו אֱמֶת וָצֶדֶק:

446

CANTILLATION OF THE HAFTARAH

Va - y'- hi .... a - ha - rey .... mos Mo-she e-ved A-do-noi

va-yo mer A-do-noi el Y'-ho-shu-a bin Nun m'-sho-res Mo-she le - mor:

Mo-she av-di mes; v'-a-to .... kum a-vor .... es ha-Yar - den .... ha-

ze, ... a - to ..... v'-hol ho-om ha-ze, ... el ho-o - - - retz,

a - sher .... o - no-hi .... no-sen lo-hem, liv-ne Yis-ro - el.

וַיְהִי אַחֲרֵי מוֹת מֹשֶׁה עֶבֶד יְהֹוָה
וַיֹּאמֶר יְהֹוָה אֶל יְהוֹשֻׁעַ בִּן נוּן,
מְשָׁרֵת מֹשֶׁה, לֵאמֹר: מֹשֶׁה עַבְדִּי
מֵת וְעַתָּה קוּם עֲבֹר אֶת-הַיַּרְדֵּן
הַזֶּה, אַתָּה וְכָל הָעָם הַזֶּה, אֶל
הָאָרֶץ, אֲשֶׁר אָנֹכִי נֹתֵן לָהֶם, לִבְנֵי
יִשְׂרָאֵל.

CANTILLATION OF "OZ YOSHIR"

O - shi-ro la-do-noi .... ki go - o go-o sus v'-ro-h'-vo ...... ro-mo va-yom.

אָשִׁירָה לַיהוָה כִּי גָאֹה גָּאָה, סוּס
וְרֹכְבוֹ רָמָה בַיָּם:

CANTILLATION OF "ESTHER"

Va-y'hi bi-mey A-hash-ve-rosh ..... hu A-hash-ve-rosh ......

ha-mo-leh me-Ho-du v'ad Kush she - - va v'-es-rim u-me-o ...... m'-di-no: ......

Ba-yo-mim ... ho-hem .... k'-she - - ves ha-me-leh A-hash-ve-rosh ......

al ki-sey mal-hu-so .... a - sher ..... b'-Shu-shan ha-bi - ro: ......

וַיְהִי בִּימֵי אֲחַשְׁוֵרוֹשׁ הוּא אֲחַשְׁוֵרוֹשׁ
הַמֹּלֵךְ מֵהֹדוּ וְעַד כּוּשׁ שֶׁבַע
וְעֶשְׂרִים וּמֵאָה מְדִינָה:
בַּיָּמִים הָהֵם כְּשֶׁבֶת הַמֶּלֶךְ
אֲחַשְׁוֵרוֹשׁ עַל כִּסֵּא מַלְכוּתוֹ
אֲשֶׁר בְּשׁוּשַׁן הַבִּירָה:

E - ho......... yosh-vo...... vo - dod............ Ho - ir......

ra - bo - si om...... Hoi - so...... k'- al - mo - no...... ra - bo - si

va - go - yim.................. So - ro - si bam-di-nos... hoi - so...... lo - mas:......

אֵיכָה יָשְׁבָה בָדָד
הָעִיר רַבָּתִי עָם
הָיְתָה כְּאַלְמָנָה רַבָּתִי בַגּוֹיִם
שָׂרָתִי בַּמְּדִינוֹת הָיְתָה לָמַס:

"AKDOMUS"

Ak - do - mus mi-lin v'sho-ro-yus shu - so. Av-lo sho-kil-no har-mon ur-shu— so.

אַקְדָּמוּת מִלִּין וְשָׁרָיוּת שׁוּתָא.
אוּלָא שָׁקֵלְנָא הַרְמָן וּרְשׁוּתָא:

449

"TAL" AND "GESHEM"

Freely sung

Yis-ga — dal.......... v'-yis-ka-dash.......... sh-mey ra-

bo..... B'- ol — mo di v'-ro hir-u-sey......... v'- yam-lih....... mal — hu — —

sey. B'- ha-ye — hon u-v'- —yo-me — hon uv — ha-yey d'hol

bes Yis-ro — el. Ba-a-go — lo u-viz-man ko-riv...... v'-im — ru o — men.

יִתְגַּדַּל וְיִתְקַדַּשׁ שְׁמֵהּ רַבָּא. בְּעָלְמָא
דִּי בְרָא כִרְעוּתֵהּ וְיַמְלִיךְ מַלְכוּתֵהּ.

בְּחַיֵּיכוֹן וּבְיוֹמֵיכוֹן וּבְחַיֵּי דְכָל בֵּית
יִשְׂרָאֵל. בַּעֲגָלָא וּבִזְמַן קָרִיב וְאִמְרוּ
אָמֵן.

450

INDEX

Index

452

453

UNITED SYNAGOGUE COMMISSION ON JEWISH EDUCATION

Azriel Eisenberg
CHAIRMAN

Leo L. Honor
VICE-CHAIRMAN

Josiah Derby
SECRETARY

Eli Bohnen
Ben Bokser
Elias Charry
Moshe Davis
Henry R. Goldberg
Morris S. Goodblatt

Jacob B. Grossman
Peretz Halpern
A. Hillel Henkin
Ario S. Hyams
Alter F. Landesman

Harry O. H. Levine
Judah Pilch
Louis L. Ruffman
Zevi Scharfstein
Samuel Sussman

Albert I. Gordon, *Executive Director, United Synagogue of America*

Abraham E. Millgram, *Educational Director, United Synagogue of America*

Simon Greenberg, *Provost, Jewish Theological Seminary of America*

Max J. Routtenberg, *Executive Vice-President, Rabbinical Assembly of America*

COMMITTEE ON MUSIC

Ario S. Hyams
CHAIRMAN

Harry Coopersmith
Judith K. Eisenstein

Abraham E. Millgram
David Putterman

Edward T. Sandrow
Robert Segal